SHERLEY'S

famous

CAT BOOK

A COMPLETE MAN[...]R

CAT OWNERS
BREEDERS
EXHIBITORS
CATTERIES
AND OTHERS

IN THE

CARE AND TREATMENT OF CATS
IN HEALTH AND IN SICKNESS

14TH EDITION

BLUE-POINTED SIAMESE & KITTENS

PREFACE

For almost a century the name SHERLEY has been synonymous with the health and happiness of dogs and cats . . . SHERLEY'S having served Royalty and Public since the reign of Queen Victoria.

This fourteenth edition of the Sherley Cat Book has been fully revised by a distinguished Veterinary Surgeon . . . and by a celebrated Breeder and Show Judge, and brought up-to-date in the light of modern research and technique, and now deals more fully than ever before with all information and all problems affecting the welfare of cats.

The Sherley Cat Book has been found in almost all countries of the world . . . in places far from the advantages of veterinary service . . . and it is our sincere hope that this book will continue to be valued as The Complete Manual for cat owners everywhere.

1965.

J.H.L.

INDEX

See also heads of Chapter Contents.

CHAPTER I
The Care of Your Cat

INTRODUCTORY NOTES

Cats are normally very healthy animals with regular appetites, clear-eyed, glossy-coated; lively and friendly members of the family; extremely lovable creatures provided they are reasonably well-treated and not ill-treated. The " family " cat is an enchanting pet and peaceful companion . . . whether a tabby of unknown origin or Siamese or Persian of prize pedigree.

Domestication and modern conditions, often coupled with incorrect or inadequate feeding, have made it impossible for cats always to keep in perfect health unaided. Impurities and toxins from the bowel become absorbed by the bloodstream and reach every part of the system through the general circulation, with detrimental effects. The nutritional products and the medicines recommended in these pages may be given with every confidence.

There are certain virus diseases which are very contagious amongst cats and are very lethal. At least one of these, Feline Infectious Enteritis, can be prevented in almost all cases by two injections carried out by a Veterinary Surgeon.

If you have a cat problem you will find the answer in this book but where serious illness is suspected correct diagnosis and treatment are urgent and important, and a Veterinary Surgeon should be consulted as soon as possible.

HISTORY

The domestication of cats dates back many thousands of years and historical records indicate that many of the present widely varied species originate from specific types. Some combine Asian and North African breeds, others isolated geographically remain somewhat true to type, although even the Siamese we know here differs from its original ancestors which were brought from Siam during the late 19th century.

Early Egyptian, Chinese and Indian history have proved the presence of cats in domestication as long as four to five thousand years ago. In early Egypt the cat was greatly valued for the protection of grain stores against rodents and there are mummified specimens of Egyptian cats showing that they were, at one period, treated almost as gods.

It is generally believed that early Phoenician traders also carried cats in their ships for the battle against rodents and they probably brought them to Britain originally. There are historical records of the presence of domestic cats in Britain as early as a thousand years ago, but later, in the middle ages, they became associated with witches and many an old woman and her pet cat were blamed for troubles and were burned together as evil spirits.

The various species would indicate that early domestic cats and wild varieties have interbred at times, although opinions differ on the subject of prime origin—and whilst it may seem logical to assume that the domestic cat has evolved from some of the original wild breeds, the few wild cats which still exist in Europe and the North of Scotland appear to be very different in size and characteristics. The wild cats of the Western U.S.A. have, in some cases, been partially domesticated in quite recent years. These are very much larger and heavier than the domestic cat and domestication has only been successful when found as very small kittens. Even so, most of them need to have their claws removed and to be kept on a lead. Wild cats do not regularly mix with the ordinary domestic cat and differ also in other characteristics such as the noise they make, which is more like a dog's bark than a cat's meow . . . and they mate only once a year.

CHARACTERISTICS & STATISTICS

The " Domestic " cat population of the United Kingdom, which includes " pedigree ", " ordinary " or " mongrel ", and also " strays and vagabonds ", totals almost 6 millions. Of these the " pedigree " breeds include about 40 varieties, shades, and classifications of the different breeds.

The " ordinary " pet cat accounts for the great majority of our cat population, but whether long-haired or short-haired, tabby or ginger, he-or-she is not by any means " ordinary ", each has his own fads and fancies and characteristics.

Of " strays and vagabonds " there are always well over half a million, living around the warehouses and docks where they usually sleep by day and hunt rats and mice at night. The descendants of cats under such circumstances generally revert to the " tabby " colouring after a few generations, but they are not wild nor do they ever seem to have the aggressive characteristics of wild cats, except in self-defence. The kittens learn to hunt at quite an early age and they are instrumental in controlling to a great extent the countrywide pest of rats and mice. Nevertheless they breed so enormously that each year the R.S.P.C.A. and other Animal Welfare Societies and Veterinary Surgeons are called upon to humanely destroy probably half a million kittens and cats.

" Domestic " cats are essentially " homing " species of animals and they do not naturally travel far from their hunting, breeding or feeding grounds except for reasons of fear or hunger. The extra-special care taken by breeders and owners of pedigree cats maintains continuity of the special breeds and types and colourings, whereas the predominating eventual reversion to " tabby " colouring after a few generations of those cats which are allowed to roam, probably accounts for the limited species of the modern " domestic " cat.

Even the " pedigree " cats themselves do in many respects each differ from their original species . . . the long-haired Persians, the Burmese, the Siamese . . . all these and other distinctive types have been carefully bred by specialists with the objectives of beauty, strength and grace.

Amongst those with special characteristics we must mention the tail-less Manx with its very unusual shape of body and " gait " . . . the Mexican hair-less cats . . . also unusual types developed from time to time, e.g. the " Rex " breed, with a short curly coat . . . and whilst all domestic cats can be trained to collar-and-lead if started from kittenhood, this is a particular feature with Siamese cats which usually become very devoted to their owners.

In ordinary home life, the well fed pet cat is not at all serious in his " mousing " efforts except on farms, where cats are usually fed on bowls of bread and milk early morning and in the afternoon to encourage them to hunt at night to find the meat they need. In any event they do need to be provided with adequate food and vitamins no matter how many rats and mice they kill . . . and also because they may be unsuccessful in their hunting. See Feeding.

The average life-span of the cat is about 12 to 15 years, although some live to the ripe age of 20, 25 and even more.

CHOOSING YOUR KITTEN

By far the majority of our domestic cats are non-pedigree, bought from or given to us by the owner of a litter, some bearing traces of their ancestry, long or short-haired, tabby, tortoiseshell or black, etc., and some partially resembling a distant Persian ancestor.

If you wish to buy a pedigree kitten however, buy one from a reputable breeder and if it is your intention to breed or to compete at shows it is worthwhile having the kitten examined by a Veterinary Surgeon before purchase. See Showing.

This paragraph deals only with the acquiring of a kitten as a pet. Because kittens are such adorable and cuddlesome creatures so many people accept a kitten on the impulse of the moment but possessing a kitten does entail the responsibility of regular feeding and comfortable housing . . . do therefore consider these things at the time of purchase. See KITTEN AT HOME.

Here are points to watch for in choosing your kitten.

Age.   He should be 8 weeks old when you will see that he has his full set of small sharp milky-white first **teeth** all showing. By this age he will be weaned and probably house-trained, also he will not be too upset by the change.

Mouth and Gums should be a nice pinky colour, the breath sweet and without any dribbling from the mouth.

Nose should be cool and slightly moist. (If warm this is usually a sign of fever). The colour of nose is usually either pink or black—if it is mottled or white this usually indicates that the kitten is not well.

Nostrils clean and without any runny or thick discharge and not sneezing. Cats and kittens are very subject to catarrh and influenza colds, which spread very quickly, and may be the forerunner of more serious disease. Never accept a kitten where any of the feline occupants of the premises appear to have colds, as all in the litter are likely to be affected within a few days. Human colds do not affect cats but the symptoms are similar—runny nose and eyes, sometimes dribbling from the mouth and sneezing, sometimes with a cough.

Eyes. A healthy kitten is bright-eyed, eyes wide open and without any of the " haw " showing, alert and playful. (See page 134).

Temperament friendly—never choose a kitten which appears to be nervous or spiteful or unfriendly or hides in a corner.

The Coat should be smooth and sleek and without any bare spots, sores or scabs on the skin. No clinging together of the fur or stickiness (indicating looseness) under the tail.

Ears. Look inside the ears to see that they are clean—smell at the inside to check for canker and examine just behind the ears where bare spots would be another indication of parasitic canker.

The Body. Run the hand over the tummy—it should not be too hard or too soft but should feel nicely firm and supple.

Breathing. Watch the cat's breathing to see if it is quiet and slow and not jerky.

If choosing a pedigree kitten, a litter in which the kittens are all of similar size usually indicates better stock than where the kittens vary in size.

Usually, although not always . . . **tortoiseshell cats** are female and **ginger cats male.** Sometimes **white cats** with blue eyes are inclined to deafness.

MALE or FEMALE KITTEN ("Doctored" or not)

The majority of those who read this chapter will be those who will love to have a cat around as a pet and a companion and to share the life of the family.

Both males and females can be operated on by a Veterinary Surgeon to prevent them breeding. In the female this is termed " spayed or neutered or doctored " . . . in the male " castrated or neutered or doctored ". An undoctored male is termed a " tom-cat " and the female a " complete-female ".

Females are usually more gentle and smaller and prettier than males but there is the problem of litters because during the spring and summer the female will almost continuously " call " the male and she may have as many as two or three litters each year . . . perhaps as many as 100 during her lifetime . . . quite a problem in the average household. Also you will have the trouble of visiting tom-cats; therefore unless you intend to breed, your female pet kitten must be neutered.

If your particular choice is a female kitten, intended purely as a pet, she should be neutered when she is 4–5 months old, which is before the first heat occurs. This is a simple and safe operation but must be carried out only by a Veterinary Surgeon. It is possible to spay later but after 6 months of age this is a much more serious and expensive operation.

A male kitten intended as a pet and companion must be neutered when he is $3\frac{1}{2}$–4 months old, otherwise when fully grown he will roam about both night and day looking for female cats, and fighting with other males, often returning home tattered and torn. Also, if not neutered, the urine of the adult male cat is very strong-smelling and objectionable and many " toms " have bad habits around the house. Although " doctored " male cats tend to put on weight and become lazy if overfed, they do make lovable and affectionate pets, but there is no need for them to become fat if correctly fed, played with, and given ample opportunity for exercise.

People who cannot afford veterinary fees for these operations can get them done with the financial assistance of the R.S.P.C.A. and other Societies, who are more than anxious to banish the populations of stray and unwanted cats by these means. Any Police Station will give you the name and address of your local R.S.P.C.A. inspector and in most towns or districts the branch secretary may be consulted on this matter in confidence.

See also SEXING.

HOUSING YOUR NEW KITTEN

Your new kitten will be rather nervous in his new home and may try to escape, therefore for the first day or two until he has settled down, you must be sure that he cannot escape. Doors and windows must be kept closed and even fireplaces should be closed in. If there is a fire in the grate then keep the grate well covered. Many a kitten has become all sooty and even scorched trying to escape up the chimney.

The only essential requirements are a soft, warm, clean bed, preferably in a box rather than a basket, slightly raised from the ground and in a corner well protected from draughts.

A comfortable size wooden box (minus the lid) turned on its side and with only a narrow board across the front 5 or 6 inches high would do. Cover the bottom with several layers of newspapers and on top of this you need an old soft cushion covered with washable material.

On arrival, particularly in cold weather, your new kitten may appreciate the extra comfort of a well-covered hot water bottle. As he grows bigger he will need a larger box or then you can buy him a permanent cat basket which should however be covered with material to eliminate draughts.

Do be sure to place the box or basket in a corner protected from draughts because cats suffer from colds and chills.

Young children handling kittens are at first inclined to squeeze and hug them too tightly and should be taught how to handle the cat gently and comfortably, to avoid injuring the kitten or getting themselves scratched, or both. Kittens and cats should never be lifted by the back of the neck. One hand underneath the chest and the other hand under and around the hindquarters, is the correct and safest method.

HOME NOTES

Never allow cats in bed . . . certain diseases, Tuberculosis, Ringworm, Sarcoptic Mange and others may be transmitted from cats to humans and vice-versa . . . therefore children or adults should never have cats in their beds.

Going on holiday . . . then it is absolutely essential to make arrangements for the necessary regular daily food, drink and exercise, at least once a day. You may perhaps be able to arrange for a relative or neighbour to go to your home each day and also to see that your cat is safely indoors each evening. Otherwise the person may take your cat to their own house . . . but extra care would be needed as he may run back to your home.

It is cruel to leave your cat alone for long periods. It is no use leaving a heap of food which you think will last your cat for days . . . he will gobble it all up in the first day or two and will then starve.

Some cats become very much devoted to their owners and may pine and become desperately ill, but if left with friends it is helpful to give the cat Sherley's Sedative Tablets during the first few days to "soothe" during the temporary change. Also, an occasional dab of Sherley's Automatic Cat Shampoo will keep him busy licking himself.

There are the alternatives of taking your cat along with you on holiday or leaving him at a boarding cattery. You can obtain the addresses of boarding centres from your local Animal Society or from your Vet.

Train your pet to wear a collar or harness from when he is quite a kitten then you will be able to take him for walks in safety. Collars worn permanently should be partly elastic so that if the cat gets it caught on a branch of a tree he can pull himself loose.

Train your kitten from an early age to allow himself to be nursed with his body completely wrapped in a rug or a small drawstring or "duffle" bag—head outside—**not** tight around the neck. This will prepare him for possible future administration of medicine or insecticides. Also open his mouth as illustrated on page 28, examine and touch his teeth with the handle of a small plastic spoon.

Train your pet also to travel in the car preferably in a basket on the floor, and to be content when left alone in the car, then you could take him with you on holiday . . . and this is often the very best solution to the problem of "going on holiday". See Travel.

When moving house . . . The simplest and safest way to ensure that your pet will not escape and try to find his way back to the old home is to treat him with Sherley's Sedative Tablets. They are quite harmless and should be given before the move and at intervals during the first 3 or 4 days exactly as stated on the carton. Moving house is so often a noisy operation and it is important to avoid your cat being startled or frightened so keep him quiet and out of the way during the moving. On arrival smear some' Automatic Cat Shampoo on his paws and legs, it will keep him busily preoccupied instead of trying to escape. Put down a few Lactol Drops occasionally to keep him busy and, if possible, keep him in one room for these first 3 or 4 days but if he is not accustomed to an indoor litter tray and refuses to use one then you will need to take him outdoors on a collar and lead, otherwise this may cause bladder trouble (cystitis).

Introducing a kitten and a puppy together into your home usually works very happily and they are excellent companions provided the first introduction is by very gentle approach and they should be carefully supervised for the first few days.

Kittens are better with the larger breeds of dogs which are more tolerant with other small pets. Take care in choosing your kitten however . . . make sure he is not of a spiteful nature and that he has not previously been chased or frightened by any dog.

Mealtimes may be troublesome at first. They should be fed from separate bowls and may in time respect one-another's dishes. Dogs have much larger mouths and tongues and gobble up their food and drink very quickly—whereas cats, being slow and dainty feeders would go hungry if both were fed from the same bowl. If necessary place the cat's food and drink on a window-sill, out of reach of the dog.

Introducing a kitten to an adult dog may not be easy unless the dog is under absolute control by word of command alone. Feline animals will instinctively arch their backs and " spit " at canines . . . . originally they were " natural " enemies . . . nevertheless you will know after a day or two whether they will become happy together in your home.

HOUSE TRAINING

Kittens need more sleep than puppies of the same age. Remember . . . kittens and cats cannot be trained by the same methods as puppies and dogs. A kitten or a cat must never be smacked as this will only frighten him and turn him wild. However, he can be coaxed and shown what is expected when training for cleanliness or how to get in and out of a high window or door flap, etc.

Your new kitten at 8 weeks will probably already have been house-trained by its mother or by the breeder but if not you should start house-training immediately on arrival.

Since you must keep your new kitten indoors for two or three days to become accustomed to its new home, even if you do eventually intend him to go outside for toilet reasons, you should house-train him in case he may have to be indoors for long periods.

All you need is a plastic or zinc litter-tray—even an old baking tin polished clean would do . . . size about 16″ × 12″ and about 3″ or 4″ deep. The tray should be filled with a ½″ layer of earth, sand, ashes, or special litter and the kitten should be put on to the tray frequently throughout the day, particularly early mornings, after meals, and whenever he awakes after sleeping.

If he scratches the earth place the tray on dry newspaper. Cats are essentially clean and the litter-tray should always be in the same place (preferably in a private corner) and at night readily accessible near his bed.

For reasons of health and hygiene the litter should be changed daily and should be sprayed with Sherley's " Deo-Odo " Cat Litter Deodorant, each time after use or at regular intervals during the day.

" Swiftie " Puppy & Kitten Trainer will simplify early house-training. It is a liquid with a particular " smell ", unnoticed by humans, and just a couple of drops are added to the tray. The kittens are placed on the tray and after a day or so they will know that this is their " spot ". Each time it is gradually moved towards the door and eventually outside. Later "Swiftie" is put on the ground at any part of the yard desired and the kitten taken there and training is complete. Breeders who train kittens this way advise new owners to put a few drops of " Swiftie " where they want the kitten to go, take the kitten there, and he will " know " automatically.

Do not ill-treat him if he offends at first and never rub your kitten's nose into it if he does make a mistake. Watch him and if you see him about to offend bang with a newspaper **on your own hand** and quickly take him to his tray—he will learn within a day or two and will never offend. The newspaper noise is also good (provided it is not so overdone as to make him nervous) to stop him playing with electric wires, needle & cotton, etc.

See Claws & Scratching.

Cat Door. There are various ways of fixing a hinged flap in the lower part of a side door . . . just large enough to allow your cat free access in or out and designed so that it does not trap his tail. Show him how it opens from both sides, and he will very quickly know the way in . . . and the way out. This is particularly convenient in wet weather.

FEEDING YOUR NEW KITTEN

This section is concerned only with the food requirements of your new kitten of 8 weeks until it reaches the adult state at about 6 or 7 months old.

At this stage your kitten is growing and developing very quickly and at first will need 4 small meals every day—at regular intervals —with plenty of fresh Lactol and also a supply of fresh water.

A good varied diet is important and should at first include tiny amounts of fresh meat, minced as finely as possible, a speck or two of mashed vegetable with fresh cooked fish, or a raw fresh egg occasionally, plenty of Lactol and Lactol Meal for building up bone and health and to avoid ailments, digestive upsets and skin troubles which so often accompany a diet which does not contain all the necessary health ingredients. Each of the mixed food meals will only need to be about an ounce or two. At the age of 8 weeks the stomach of the kitten is very tiny and of course the meals will need to be well mashed and free from bone and can be gradually increased in quantity.

In their original state cats were carnivorous, feeding mainly on small animals, therefore it will be appreciated that meat is their main food. Many people think that cats can live on fish alone but this is incorrect and in fact **too much fish is harmful** and can cause skin troubles and digestive upsets and at the kitten stage fish should not be given more than at one of the meals each day. As they grow older then fish should be given on alternate days only.

Your kitten will need to be introduced to **vegetables** very gradually at first, just a small piece of mashed carrot or a small brussel sprout leaf minced and mashed, mixed in with the food and gravy at one of the meals each day and gradually increased.

In the early stages of feeding it is good to add the vitamins contained in Sherley-Vite Tablets—at first half a tablet crumbled and sprinkled on food provides additional vitamins and minerals and as he grows he can have a whole tablet each day.

Cats and Kittens need to eat **grass** and for those who live in town flats a seed box in which grass is grown is the simple answer. Many cats, particularly those which are overfed, get a bit liverish at times and can be seen biting off pieces of grass blades and swallowing them, usually followed by slight vomiting and this is also their natural way of getting rid of hair and other matter in the throat, after which they feel better. There is no objection to this habit other than the mess but it is not known whether the eating of grass has any other advantages. A once weekly dose of Lik-a-med Laxative is preferable and avoids the vomiting. Please note . . . **never** give Castor Oil to cats or kittens.

When feeding young kittens the litter tray should be close to the food tray, moving this further away, in stages, then to the position where it will normally be kept.

DIET SHEET FOR KITTENS

8–16 weeks—4 meals a day

BREAKFAST—Lactol with Lactol Meal well mixed together like a porridge.

LUNCH — Gravy over a little very finely chopped cooked or good raw meat and a speck of potato and greens mashed together.

TEA — Lactol over Lactol Meal and Energol, together with half a Sherley-Vite Tablet crumbled and mixed in.

SUPPER — A little cooked mashed fish (be sure there are no bones) . . . or egg yolk with Lactol.

16 weeks to 7 months. 3 meals a day.

As the kitten gradually grows to adulthood at about 7 months, you will need to vary the meals and size and remember that fish must not be given more than once a day and that it should be cooked and with all the bones removed. Or give tinned fish—a sardine or two, or herrings in tomato sauce. The latter sometimes does not please the palate of the kitten on account of the sauce flavouring added but the various canned fish available and also any of the good brands of tinned cat food should be introduced to the diet early in life so that he does not become too " choosey " in his food.

It is important to remember that from the kitten stage onwards the food should be gradually increased to as much as he consumes in the 10 or 15 minutes normal feeding time. The food should not be left around otherwise he will be inclined to repeatedly eat and grow extra fat apart from the possible contamination of food by flies etc. Do not endanger the health or life of your kitten or cat by giving him stale or unclean food and always make sure that the dishes are thoroughly washed after each meal. Be as careful with his food and dishes as you would be for yourself.

See also Feeding Baby Kittens.

FEEDING ADULT CATS

Originally, in their wild state, cats were exclusively flesh eaters (meat and fish) and whilst our domestic cats love both meat and fish this does not usually include all the **essential vitamin and mineral diet requirements.** Therefore the diet should be wide and varied to provide the complete range of their nutritional requirements and certain foods need to be given with care and with limitations. Cats prefer their foods warm and most cats will refuse " frig-cold " foods also because the smell is " sealed in " until the food is warmed up.

A cat with even a slight cold will often refuse his normal food because he cannot smell it.

Quantity of Food. The total daily requirements of the average size adult cat would be about 5–6 oz. of meat or game—or about 7–8 oz. of fish—**split into 2 main meals, morning and evening,** and as a general rule meat should comprise about 75 % of the diet, plus milk or Lactol, and also water. See also Nursing Queens.

Beef or Mutton should be fresh and may be given raw or minced or cooked.

Horsemeat must always be cooked unless it is absolutely fresh and of the grade guaranteed fit for human consumption.

Wild rabbit must always be thoroughly well cooked because some parts may contain parasites such as the intermediate stage of the Tapeworm. Remove all bones.

Domestic rabbit is usually safe to feed lightly cooked or raw and without bones.

Liver. A small portion of cooked liver may be given but not more than once weekly. Any liver that is pale and " spotted " should not be given.

Lights may be given if well cooked, but they are of little real food value as they contain very little nourishment.

Fish is an essential part of the cat's diet but a cat must not be fed on fish only as this tends to cause eczema. Fish must be clean and untainted by flies and must be given cooked. **Fish must be fresh, not salted.** Tinned fish may be given occasionally.

Removing bones. All rabbit, game and fish bones should be removed . . . it is in fact advisable also to remove bones from all cooked meats.

Raw beef bones. Marrow bones may be given, preferably with scraps of meat still on the bone. Gnawing at such a bone is excellent for the cat's teeth.

Cereals and cooked vegetables in small quantities at first, should be mixed in with minced meat or fish from an early age. A crumbled Sherley-Vite tablet sprinkled in with any meal once a day adds extra essential vitamins and will make the vegetables more readily acceptable.

A milky meal or breakfast may be given of Lactol with Lactol Meal or Biscuits or " Liver-Snaps ". Lactol is particularly valuable in the rearing of healthy youngsters—and for nursing mothers and invalid and elderly cats. Lactol Drops are also a welcome " tit-bit ".

Drinking Water. A supply of clean cold water should also be within reach at all times. As so much water is chlorinated nowadays, it is best to take the drinking water from the hot tap and put it down when it is cold. The chlorine evaporates more readily when it is in hot water and the water is therefore more palatable to the cat when it has become cold.

Remove unfinished meals left over after your cat has finished eating, to avoid contamination by flies. It is in fact desirable to remove any food left over if, after your cat has had about 15 minutes feeding time, he has left his feeding bowl completely.

REGULAR CONDITIONING

The prevention of illness can be attained by the cultivation of good health, and is obviously preferable to the curative treatment of illness, and far more humane as well as less distressing and less costly for the owner. Some of the more serious cat complaints can be prevented by injections whilst those not preventable are obviously better withstood by a healthy cat. The essential vitamins in " Sherley-Vites ", given regularly—a two-day course each week —will greatly assist in maintaining first-class condition. Natural resistance to germs and parasites is then at its best, the harmful and dangerous effect of illness is less, convalescence is speedier and more complete.

In avoiding illness hygiene also plays an important part, but in addition to external care it is essential that the system be kept in proper working order. A once-weekly dose of Lik-a-Med Laxative Cream assists nature in eliminating impurities from the bowels and also prevents accumulation of hair (or hair-ball) in the stomach or bowels, so often the cause of distress and frequently necessitating a surgical operation. See Hair-ball.

GROOMING

Start training your kitten to allow you to comb and brush him almost the first day you bring him home because, to maintain the skin and coat in perfect and beautiful condition, regular daily grooming is essential, particularly with long-haired cats. The cat's tongue, being papillous (rough surfaced), acts almost like a brush but although he normally keeps his coat clean by continually licking it, loose hairs must be combed out daily to prevent matting and tangling and to avoid your cat suffering from Hair-ball (accumulation of hair in the stomach).

Daily grooming also enables you to watch his general skin condition and to check whether any parasites are present. For grooming you will need a good quality steel comb without rough or sharp points, to avoid scratching the skin. For long-haired cats a long toothed rake-like comb and a nylon brush . . . for short-haired cats a smaller toothed comb and a brush or leather.

The skin itself is continually shed and as in humans the skin needs cleaning and stimulating to keep it healthy and virile and this can be achieved by a weekly beauty treatment with Coatacine, sprinkled on a rough cloth and massaged into the coat and skin. Healthy skin promotes the growth of a healthy and lovely coat. If your cat is correctly fed with a good varied diet and if he is not otherwise ill, the **scurf and dull coat** are quickly improved by application and massage with Coatacine . . . combined with the tonic vitamins of Sherley-Vite Tablets; just one each day to improve the general condition. See also Worms.

Moulting of the coat is influenced by light and temperature and usually takes place in the late spring to early summer with the warmer weather and the longer days . . . and some also shed their summer coat in the late autumn. During moulting extra-special attention to **thorough daily combing** out of the dead hair is then necessary, particularly on long-haired cats, to avoid the hairs being shed or rubbed off on furnishings, clothing, etc.

Matting of the hair can be partly broken up by working with the fingers, completing the task with a metal comb.

When the matting is severe however, separation is quite a long and difficult task. Use a sharp-pointed instrument such as the blade of a pair of scissors, pointed away from the body, to puncture through the mats and gently tear them apart, then comb out.

22

A badly-tangled coat needs a great deal of time and patience but as your cat will not allow this rigorous attention for any length of time, **do a little at a time allowing him 10 or 15 minutes between each session of grooming.** The task should, however, be completed as soon as possible because the longer the tangles are left the worse they become. If it is necessary to trim off any of the hair this will soon grow again. In the case of **neglected long-haired cats with masses of tangles** this is an almost impossible task without hurting your cat and causing him to struggle dangerously and unless you have trained your cat to be shampooed from kitten-hood then it is best to give him a Sherley's Dog and Cat Sedative Tablet half an hour before starting to comb him. If he is still difficult take him to a Veterinary Surgeon who can give a light anaesthetic and comb out the matted fur without any distress to the cat.

Wet Paint. Owing to the possible danger of causing skin troubles, it is not advisable to use turpentine or chemicals. It is best to cleanse away as much as possible with butter and wipe off, then shampoo and rinse the part. Any hair which has to be cut off will quickly grow again.

For Tar on the feet. Some cats will not mind their paws being cleansed with just a drop of Eucalyptus oil mixed with a spot of butter and rubbed with the corner of a cloth . . . then washed and dried. Sherley's Dry Bath used in the same way will clean off very thin or greasy tar stains.

Hardened paint usually needs to be trimmed out of the coat as described on the previous page under " When the matting is severe ".

Prevention is better than cure . . . Whether short or long-haired your cat will always look more lovely and will be tangle-free with regular daily grooming.

Grease or oil on the coat can be cleansed quickly with Sherley's Dry-Bath, applied on a cloth, taking care to clean the hair only, without too much wetting of the skin.

Normally a cat will wash itself every day but there are times when a cat may be " off-colour " and omits this regular cleaning habit. This is also the case in elderly and invalid cats and Sherley's have now introduced an " Automatic " Cat Shampoo which stimulates and encourages such cats to lick themselves, although obviously this cannot help in cases of severe matting or paint, etc. See also WASHING, overleaf.

WASHING

Cats do like water and they do enjoy being shampooed provided they are accustomed to bathing from when they are young.

Although it is not usually necessary to shampoo a cat, as you will have learned from notes on grooming, the necessity may arise and many breeders do bath cats before Showing, to loosen the dead hairs and to thoroughly cleanse the skin.

The shampoo is given a few days before the Show to allow time for natural grease to return and adequate grooming to make the fur stand up.

If you have a long-haired cat, and particularly if it is white or very light coloured, then it is a good plan to get him used to an occasional bath from when he is quite a baby then he will enjoy it because cats are not really frightened of water . . . everything depends upon how you carry out the bathing and how early in life you start. Until your cat is used to bathing it may take 2 persons and the door should be kept closed.

First of all do remember that cats can easily catch cold during or after a bath, therefore you must take care to avoid draughts, even on a warm day . . . it is always best to bath him indoors and in a warm atmosphere. Secondly you must be sure to dry him absolutely thoroughly after the bath. In winter the bath should be the very last thing at night—**after** he has been out.

The water should be blood heat—test the heat with your elbow as you would when bathing a baby—about 100°F (= 38°C)—it should feel just comfortably warm. The sink is the best place, preferably with a pad at the bottom and only about an inch or two of water. Before you put him into the water wet his feet with your hands then stand him in the water. Talk to him and gently smooth him over with the water underneath then over his back **without wetting his ears, nose and face.** Now gently massage in the shampoo adding water from the basin, washing and thoroughly massaging the skin.

Finally rinse thoroughly either by hand or from the basin or a jug . . . you must rinse thoroughly (don't use soap as this is most difficult to rinse out). Be sure the water is still warm.

Bathing even a young kitten is absolutely harmless provided you wrap and dry thoroughly and keep him warm and cosy for at least an hour after the bath.

Washing the tail. Most cats get their tails very dirty and scurfy and it is very necessary to wash their tails regularly, particularly tom cats. The best way is to sit the cat on plenty of newspaper at the side of the draining board, his tail in a jug of mixed warm shampoo and wash the tail all over, then rinse with two or three lots of fresh warm water in the jug. Dry thoroughly and keep him indoors for an hour or two.

Use only a shampoo which is specifically suitable for cats—or for dogs and cats—such as Amplex Deodorant Shampoo.

CARE OF THE EARS

Prevention is better than cure and a little regular attention will avoid most of the inner ear irritations caused by the ear-mange mite which so often leads to the cat scratching at its ear, thereby causing even more complications, often with injury to the ear flap. An occasional puff of Sherley's Canker Powder inside the ear will avoid many of the troubles such as Canker.

See EAR ailments, injuries and treatments.

CARE OF THE EYES

A watery discharge from the eyes is often a symptom of chill or cat distemper or injury and at the first signs, minor maladies can often be cleared by cleansing the eyes with warm Sherley's Eye Lotion on cotton wool . . . or a few drops may be dropped into the eye by squeezing the cotton wool. Always use a clean piece for each eye—and a separate fresh clean piece if the cotton-wool is used as a dropper. See details of EYE ailments, injuries and treatments, also Kittens' Eyes.

CARE OF THE NOSE

The nose of the healthy cat usually feels cool and just slightly moist, without any wetness or discharge from the nostrils. Any sneezing combined with discharge from the nose are usually indications of some disease. The nose may also be bathed with Eye Lotion or with warm water if there is any discharge.

See Treatment of Illness, Influenza and Distemper.

CARE OF THE TEETH

Kittens are born without teeth and some of their first (milk) teeth begin to show at 4 weeks and by the time they are 8 weeks old they should have their full sets of top and lower teeth, 26 teeth in all.

Starting at 5 or 6 months the second (adult) teeth begin to push out the baby teeth just as in humans. In cats the process is very rapid and quite a strain on the young cat, sometimes causing indigestion, loss of weight or teething-fever and in some cases teething fits. **If teething fits occur** give him half of a Sherley's Sedative Tablet and keep him warm in a quiet and dark corner. Occasionally a milk tooth might persist and may need to be extracted by an expert breeder or Veterinary Surgeon. Repeated fits may also be due to Worms.

A raw, meaty, soft rib bone and a few Lactol Biscuits or Liver Snaps once or twice a week will aid the development of the second teeth and in fact these items of food given regularly will help to prevent many of the mouth and teeth troubles throughout the whole life of your cat. The stomach of the normal healthy adult cat can digest solids of bone within an hour or two and the process of gnawing at bone and hard biscuit prevents the formation of tartar on the teeth which may cause complications such as mouth ulcers, pyorrhoea, etc.

Examine your cat's mouth and teeth at regular intervals and watch for these faults . . .

Bad breath . . . Indicating some disease of the gums, tartar or disorder of the digestion. See Pyorrhoea and Gastritis.

Sore Gums . . . Any bright red or purple inflammation may be due to abscess or a fragment of bone or even a needle embedded in the gum.

Loose or Broken Teeth . . . These need to be extracted and if quite loose they may be extracted by the fingers, or by tooth forceps, but if they are broken then veterinary attention is best.

Tartar . . . This may build up in a hard brownish lime deposit on the teeth to a thickness 1/16th″ or more, pushing back the gums so that food debris and germs accumulate causing inflammation, foul breath and pain and the cat avoids hard foods, dribbles and may refuse all solid foods. See TEETH-DISEASES, etc. Light deposits of Tartar can be removed regularly by gradually chipping it away with a small tooth scaler and cracking it off with small tooth extractor forceps. During the process the cat needs to be gagged to keep his mouth open.

If the scaling is too difficult for home operation take the cat along to your Veterinary Surgeon.

Tooth Forceps

Loss of Teeth . . . Usually due to absence of essential vitamins, minerals, etc., in the diet. See DIET.

Foreign Object Stuck in Mouth . . . If your cat is off his food, or toys with his food and appears to have a good appetite, going

repeatedly to his food dish but not eating properly then the reason is probably that he has some sharp object embedded in his mouth or tongue—or even a rubber band round his tongue, or if he chews only on one side of the mouth he may have toothache.

It is a good plan to accustom your cat to letting you examine his mouth, tongue and teeth regularly . . . right from when he is a young kitten.

CARE OF THE CLAWS

The claws of the cat are retractible and when walking are withdrawn but when the cat does not have much opportunity for regular outdoor exercise and scratching at trees or fences then there is a tendency for the tips of the claws to become overgrown. This will cause discomfort and he will claw at anything suitable within the house . . . curtains, carpets, furniture, etc.

Every kitten or cat kept mainly indoors should be provided with a **scratching-post** . . . a stout wide board about 18″ to 24″ long (according to size of kitten or cat), covered with several layers of strong sacking or sail-cloth securely nailed or sewn on . . . or a half round log with the bark still on, or covered in the same way. Train your kitten or cat to use the scratching-post by placing him on or near it whenever you notice him scratching. Kittens learn very quickly but when cats have acquired bad habits this training requires more time and patience.

Cutting the claws. In each claw there is a vein and a nerve and only the very transparent tip of about one-sixteenth to one-eighth of an inch (2 millimetres) may be cut off and this quickly grows again so that cutting is a regular weekly task. It is important that only the very tip is cut, because the " quick " of the claw is very near and once accidentally cut you can say " goodbye " to further nail trimming for it is extremely painful to the cat and he will never forget the experience. The introduction of a scratching-post is a much wiser and far safer method but . . . if cutting is essential then **do not use scissors** as these would tend to tear or break the nail . . . use only the small circular nail clippers which are specially made for cats and small dogs.

Circular
Nail Cutters

CHAPTER II
Breeding

INTRODUCTORY FACTS

Assuming that you are **new to breeding** but have little knowledge of cats . . . or that your pet cat is about to present you with a litter . . . we start this chapter with facts about cats.

After her first litter a female cat which has not been spayed (doctored) is generally called a " queen " by cat fanciers. The doctored female is called a " neutered or spayed female ". The complete male cat is called a " tom " and the castrated male a " neutered or doctored tom ".

For those who contemplate regular **breeding of thorough-breds as a hobby and for showing,** it is advisable to join your local " Cat Fancy " club and gain the benefit of advice and experience of one or more of the members and you will find this a wonderfully gratifying if not very lucrative hobby. Many of the most beautiful show specimens are reared by cat lovers who breed as a hobby rather than for profit.

There is very little profit in cat-breeding as a business and indeed cats usually do much better in small numbers, but for those who intend breeding pedigree cats as a **business,** a thorough working knowledge of all aspects of the business is absolutely essential. First class show cats are expensive and it is therefore desirable to spend some time working at a cattery or with a breeder to gain professional experience as otherwise lack of knowledge could endanger the expensive stock by simple mistakes in the omission of necessary precautions to avoid diseases or epidemics.

OESTRUM " Season " or " Heat "

From the age of about 6 months onwards or maybe even earlier in Siamese, queens come into oestrus (season, or on-heat) at frequent intervals during each Spring and Summer—some as often as every three or four weeks if not mated. The duration of the " heat " in most breeds lasts about 4 to 6 days (Siamese 8–12 days). Different queens vary in their behaviour before and during the " season ", but in general the indications are as follows . . .

A day or two before the season actually starts there is swelling of the vulva (under the tail), the cat becomes restless and the appetite is greater than usual.

During the next 2 or 3 days she becomes much more affectionate, rubbing her cheeks against person's legs. There will still be a slight discharge varying from clear to pink or red from the vulva but as the cat continually licks herself clean this may pass unnoticed.

She will start " calling " in a wailing tone to attract a male and although she will try everything possible to escape, during this stage she may refuse to mate.

During the next 2 or 3 days the calling is more persistent, in fact almost continuous . . . the desire for fondling may now become a nuisance . . . the cat rolls on the floor . . . " treads " the ground with her hind legs, sometimes in a crouching position. She will rush around " calling " at the windows and doors, which will attract the males of the neighbourhood to the doors and garden and she will escape at the first opportunity. The vulva is more swollen and hot and there is a more coloured discharge. She will accept the male, and if out of doors will mate several times during these particular days, with the same or with different sires.

Mating actually takes place during the last mentioned stage, usually 4 or 5 days after the season starts, but each individual queen varies. The duration of the heat in most breeds lasts about 4–6 days.

After the season has finished the unusual behaviour and the discharge will cease, the vulva will have returned to normal and the local " tom " cats will no longer be interested.

If the queen has not mated during the season, she will come on heat again after just a few weeks (some even as soon as two weeks) and will continue in this way repeatedly, which means in effect that she would be on heat for about 7 days almost every 2 or 3 months throughout the year . . . and if for these reasons it is decided that no litters are desired at all, and the cat is wanted purely as a pet, then your Veterinary Surgeon should be consulted regarding spaying whilst she is young, because a restrained queen could become temperamental—possibly vicious.

From the age of 12 months however a queen may be **mated once or twice every year,** preferably in the Spring and Summer, so that the young kittens may have the benefit of warm fresh air and sunshine out of doors as they progress through the weaning and the playful " kittenish " stages.

If it is **not desired to mate** the queen, then extra-special precautions are necessary to prevent her escaping—she will do so at the very first opportunity and will not return until she has been mated, therefore often it is best to keep her in a small room and give her an occasional dose of Sherley's Sedative Tablets until the season finishes, so that she does not become difficult or wear herself out.

MATING

It is not advisable to allow a female cat to mate until her second season when she is about 10 months old and if she is strong and healthy and normal size for her age she should not be restrained more than two seasons without being mated. To keep a full size healthy precocious female cat without mating until 12 months old or more would be very unwise because she may grow difficult to handle and spiteful to her owner.

An undersized or weakly female should however be restrained until her third season and in the meantime she should be nourished with Lactol and Lintox and one Sherley-Vite Tablet each day to build up her strength.

Queen cats may be mated once or twice a year until 8 or 9 years of age. With pedigree cats (the long-haired in particular) it may not be possible to get two matings in if the first litter is late in the summer. Mating should take place only when your queen cat is in the best of health and she should be started on a course of " Sherley-Vites " for a month or two beforehand.

If it is intended to breed the best time is just after the coloured discharge ceases and usually the third day of her calling. It is preferable to mate early in the spring and have the benefit of the warmer weather, fresh air and exercise, in the summer sunshine whilst the kittens are young.

At first matings it is not advisable to mate young with young . . . either the female or the male should be experienced. Care should also be exercised in choosing the pedigree of the stud cat to ensure good quality progeny and if possible expert advice is desirable, or alternatively some acquaintance with the exhibition class of previous progeny of the stud.

During mating the two cats should first be " introduced " in separate adjoining pens and after a while they may then be together in a room or enclosure where they can be kept under observation by the breeder and separated after mating. If the timing is correct they will mate quite satisfactorily and two matings should be allowed, evening then morning and preferably within 24 hours.

Females taken to stud for mating. The appointment will need to be arranged in advance. The breeder will advise the actual stage of " season " when the queen is to be brought and she will need to be left with the breeder who will advise the owner of the queen exactly when she should be collected and will provide pedigree and other details.

For at least a week afterwards the queen should be kept indoors and away from all " toms " because she may still be mated by any prowling tom and such subsequent matings can fertilise and include other kittens in the same litter.

Arranging a FOSTER-MOTHER in case of need

Breeders of valuable pedigrees try to make arrangements for a foster-mother at the same time or a few days before the thoroughbred mating in case there may be some feeding trouble or other misfortune at the kittening time.

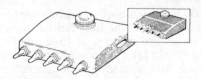

ARTIFICIAL FOSTER-MOTHER

These can be purchased from Arnold & Sons Veterinary Instruments Ltd., 54 Wigmore St., London, W.1.

THE STUD CAT

To owners of stud cats. All visiting females must have been vaccinated against infectious enteritis and the owner of the visiting female may be required to bring along for inspection the veterinary certificate of inoculation and the visiting female should be carefully examined on arrival. If any signs of disease are present the cat concerned should be returned to the owner at once. It is obviously better to miss a stud fee than to risk the introduction of cat cold or flu or mange, for instance, into a cattery. In this connection it is advisable to mention especially parasitic canker of the ear, a most contagious ailment.

Stud cats should not be used for breeding purposes at all until the age of 12 months onwards, when they are then fully mature and developed, although many are not fully fertile until they are about 18 months. Inadequate diet, starting too young or too frequent stud use can affect their progeny throughout their whole breeding life. Stud cats are at their best up to about four years of age and even up to 9 or 10 years, if carefully managed.

The stud cat will need an extra-special **raw meat diet** from kittenhood onwards. See Feeding, pages 20–21. **He should not be treated as a pet** even when he is a kitten because when he is old enough to breed he will need to be housed entirely on his own, in a large, hygienic, strong, pen with sleeping quarters and a large size run away from other cats and people. Also, unless it is intended to accept visiting queens it is essential to keep 3 or 4 or even more queens for mating otherwise he may become a nuisance to the neighbours and may become savage.

It is therefore important to bear all of these facts in mind before contemplating the acquisition of a stud cat for pedigree breeding. See also Cryptorchidism and Sterility.

PREPARING FOR KITTENING

When in kitten, the first signs are usually three or four weeks after the mating when the nipples are more pinky in colour and at about 6 weeks she starts to become plump. Her appetite will have increased and she will repel any tom cats, in fact she should be kept away from toms as they may attack her.

It is essential that the queen should be free from worms and she should be " wormed " any time between the second and sixth weeks after mating. This is quite safe with Sherley's Roundworm Tablets for Cats or Sherley's Worming Cream and will prevent the mother passing on the eggs of worms (which would otherwise be present in her milk) to the kittens, where they proceed to develop in the bowels of the kittens from birth and retard their health and progress. Unborn kittens have been shown to have these worms already in the body before birth. Whilst the roundworms do not worry adult cats they are transmitted to the unborn kittens in the uterus via the bloodstream.

After the worming treatment, it is advisable to avoid later worm infestations by correct feeding and reasonably careful control in hygiene and mixing with other cats. See ROUNDWORMS.

In **long-haired** breeds it is advisable to **cut away the hair from around the breasts** so that they do not become matted, and to enable the kittens to feed more easily.

If the breasts do become caked, wash them with Sherley's Antiseptic Lotion or Amplexol diluted with warm water and grease them with a little Vaseline.

During the pregnancy, the queen's skin should be kept healthy and free from insects by the use of Vamoose Pet Powder, sparingly applied exactly as directed on the tin, as it is important that all insects should be got rid of well before the kittens are born.

Lactol should be given daily during pregnancy to ensure ample milk for feeding the kittens . . . the Vitamin D content enables the expectant mother to assimilate the lime salts in her food, thereby ensuring that the kittens are born with sound bone, firm flesh and the foundations of good teeth.

Provided the **bowels** act regularly no purgative medicine is required until two days before the kittens are due, then a dose of Sherley's Lik-a-Med Laxative Cream should be given. Rest is important and she should have her normal diet and over-feeding should be avoided.

Normal **exercise** is desirable but preferably without any tree-climbing particularly during the last 2 or 3 weeks. Handle her gently and avoid any handling of her tummy as the kittens can be so easily injured . . . in fact, cats in kitten are best left in peace, with the minimum of fondling or handling.

Your cat will need to have a **warm secluded darkened place** where she can have her kittens and she is likely to choose a bedroom cupboard or other inconvenient place, therefore about 7–10 days before the kittens are due arrange a low wooden box, about 18″ × 24″ with the front only about 4″ high, filled with newspapers. The mother and kittens will remain in the box until the kittens are 8 or 9 weeks old, therefore a good size box is desirable. Place this in a suitable  position of your own choice safely away from the family and other pets, preferably in a draught-free, dark and quiet cupboard, as the **kittens are born blind and must not be subjected to strong light until their eyes are open.** She should be taken to the box repeatedly, with a saucer of Lactol, until she appreciates the spot you have chosen; but do not close her in against her will, because afterwards when all the kittens are born elsewhere she is quite likely to transfer them, one by one, to the place of her own choice.

Before kittening—particularly queens which have had kittens before—the **nipples** may need some attention. Wash with diluted Amplexol or Sherley's Antiseptic Lotion and then a little Vaseline or liquid paraffin put on to remove any dry skin or dirt.

A cat in kitten is best left alone quietly and as the birth draws near she will begin tearing up the newspaper and making up a nest in her box, purring all the while. There should now be some signs of milk in the nipples and as a cat usually gives birth to her kittens without difficulty she is best left alone with only occasional careful observation in case of any difficulties—which may necessitate veterinary assistance.

35

KITTENING—GESTATION

The average period for which a cat carries her young (period of gestation) varies according to breed, usually about 9 weeks . . . Siamese $9\frac{1}{2}$ weeks.

The Gestation Table on page 39 based on 9 weeks (63 days) may vary anything from 3 or 4 days or even more, earlier or later. There is no need to worry if the arrival is a few days late provided the cat appears happy and well. Kittens born before the 56th day are regarded as premature.

The cat is one of the most efficient of mothers and if undisturbed and without complications normally takes her kittening procedure in calm methodical fashion purring all the time. By her straining of the abdomen combined with muscular contraction of the uterus, she expels her kittens complete with the placenta, which is the " afterbirth " or " sac " inside which each of the kittens is carried. As each kitten is expelled she immediately bites open the sac to release the liquid within and to allow the kitten to breathe, otherwise it could not survive. Then she proceeds to cleanse the kitten all over and herself cleans up much of the liquid and the afterbirth which do actually contain natural nourishment.

During the labour she will need only a bowl or saucer of Lactol or water placed outside the nest box but near enough for her to reach without leaving the box.

Many breeders of valuable pedigree cats watch that the mother does perform her natural duty of puncturing the sac quickly and if this is neglected they " pinch " open the sac with the fingers and also wipe over the mouth and nose of the kitten with moistened cotton-wool but this is really best left to the mother. Many also remove an occasional sac so that the mother does not consume too many. The minimum of interference however is best.

Labour normally takes 1 or 2 hours for the first kitten to arrive and they are usually born at intervals of about 20 minutes. An average litter is about five kittens and the mother may even rest awhile after the first two or three and provided she is not straining without result, or distressed, then all is well.

If it is noticed that labour has commenced and the mother is continuously **straining or is distressed or keeps leaving her nest,** and that no kittens arrive within the course of two or three hours, unless you have had practical experience it is advisable to obtain the assistance of a Veterinary Surgeon.

If however she is straining for more than 30 minutes between births without result then a kitten may have become blocked and Veterinary help may be urgently necessary but if the kitten's head has reached the exterior and is visible and final expulsion is unduly delayed, there is no objection (after thoroughly washing and then rinsing the hands in a good disinfectant such as diluted Sherley's Antiseptic Lotion or wearing a clean washed glove or using a clean cloth) in gently grasping the kitten behind the ears and pulling very gently outwards and downwards, preferably at the same moments as the mother is straining. At the same time very gently and slowly rotate the kitten first to the left and then to the right, not more than about 30 degrees. This often helps to effect a clearance of the " jam ". The same applies if the kitten arrives tail first, but do not grasp the limbs for the pulling, rather try to get a finger and thumb in front of the stifle joints, thus pulling the whole body, particularly when rotation is attempted.

It may happen that any one of the kittens may become blocked, as above mentioned, therefore it is always desirable to keep occasional watch on the progress in case assistance is needed and those who are inexperienced should obtain skilled or qualified Veterinary help when this appears necessary.

It is not recommended that any breeder should resort to the use of Obstetric Forceps unless he has had some veterinary training and the following notes are included only for the benefit of overseas breeders in very remote districts or for those who live some considerable distance from the nearest Veterinary Surgeon.

In such cases the breeder should provide himself with a pair of the Cat Obstetric Forceps or **smallest size** Whelping Forceps as used for toy dogs. With the aid of these, invaluable assistance may be rendered in emergency, in the event of a queen having difficulty in giving birth to her kittens.

In cases of such emergency where veterinary assistance is not available an amateur can remove a kitten from the passage with the small Obstetric Forceps and it is wise for those who have a number of cats to keep this instrument handy. Before using the forceps the position of the kitten within the passage should be carefully ascertained.

Obstetric Forceps for cats, 5½″ stainless steel, obtainable from Arnold Veterinary Instruments Ltd., 54 Wigmore St., London, W.1.

Wearing rubber gloves if possible, thoroughly wash and scrub the hands with soap and diluted Amplexol or Sherley's Antiseptic Lotion, and dry them. Smear the fingers with Obstetric Cream. (Obstetric Cream is best because it is sterile. It can be obtained from chemists but in emergency clean fresh Vaseline may have to be used). Lubricate this well into the passage and pass the forefinger into the passage. When the position of the kitten has been ascertained smear the points of the Obstetric Forceps with the cream and guide them by a well-greased finger into the passage to the obstructing kitten, which should be gently but firmly gripped. The finger should then be passed round the head of the forceps to make certain that they enclose nothing but the kitten, and a firm hold having been obtained the kitten should be pulled in a slightly downward direction each time the queen strains. A slow steady pull should be given with no jerking, and the operation should not be hurried.

Disinfect the hands and forceps by rinsing in a weak solution of Amplexol or Sherley's Antiseptic Fluid (it is good to prepare a bowl of diluted solution ready in advance) and if it is necessary to remove more than one kitten, the rinsing should be repeated between each removal.

After using Whelping Forceps in assisting the births, when all the kittens appear to have been delivered it is advisable to gently feel the outside of the abdomen with fingers on one side and thumb on the other, where an unborn kitten which may be left can be felt, or a placenta retained inside, and this latter can usually be washed out by a warm water douche.

After all the kittens are born and the mother has completed her own cleansing operations and has left the box, this is the time to gently rearrange her bedding, removing all soiled materials, wiping around her box with the minimum of disturbance to mother and kittens. A piece of thick clean blanket, which can be washed, is best . . . and an extra piece in reserve for changing, as the mother may continue to have some discharge for about 10 to 14 days afterwards.

Some mothers resent any disturbance during the first day or two and may even move or kill the whole litter therefore any changing or attention should be carried out in semi-darkness and with the minimum of disturbance.

Cat Breeder's Dates Calculator

(Gestation Table)

Served January	Due to Kitten March	Served February	Due to Kitten April	Served March	Due to Kitten May	Served April	Due to Kitten June	Served May	Due to Kitten July	Served June	Due to Kitten August	Served July	Due to Kitten September	Served August	Due to Kitten October	Served September	Due to Kitten November	Served October	Due to Kitten December	Served November	Due to Kitten January	Served December	Due to Kitten February
1	5	1	5	1	3	1	3	1	3	1	3	1	2	1	3	1	3	1	3	1	3	1	2
2	6	2	6	2	4	2	4	2	4	2	4	2	3	2	4	2	4	2	4	2	4	2	3
3	7	3	7	3	5	3	5	3	5	3	5	3	4	3	5	3	5	3	5	3	5	3	4
4	8	4	8	4	6	4	6	4	6	4	6	4	5	4	6	4	6	4	6	4	6	4	5
5	9	5	9	5	7	5	7	5	7	5	7	5	6	5	7	5	7	5	7	5	7	5	6
6	10	6	10	6	8	6	8	6	8	6	8	6	7	6	8	6	8	6	8	6	8	6	7
7	11	7	11	7	9	7	9	7	9	7	9	7	8	7	9	7	9	7	9	7	9	7	8
8	12	8	12	8	10	8	10	8	10	8	10	8	9	8	10	8	10	8	10	8	10	8	9
9	13	9	13	9	11	9	11	9	11	9	11	9	10	9	11	9	11	9	11	9	11	9	10
10	14	10	14	10	12	10	12	10	12	10	12	10	11	10	12	10	12	10	12	10	12	10	11
11	15	11	51	11	13	11	13	11	13	11	13	11	12	11	13	11	13	11	13	11	13	11	12
12	16	12	16	12	14	12	14	12	14	12	14	12	13	12	14	12	14	12	14	12	14	12	13
13	17	13	17	13	15	13	15	13	15	13	15	13	14	13	15	13	15	13	15	13	15	13	14
14	18	14	18	14	16	14	16	14	16	14	16	14	15	14	16	14	16	14	16	14	16	14	15
15	19	15	19	15	17	15	17	15	17	15	17	15	16	15	17	15	17	15	17	15	17	15	16
16	20	16	20	16	18	16	18	16	18	16	18	16	17	16	18	16	18	16	18	16	18	16	17
17	21	17	21	17	19	17	19	17	19	17	19	17	18	17	19	17	19	17	19	17	19	17	18
18	22	18	22	18	20	18	20	18	20	18	20	18	19	18	20	18	20	18	20	18	20	18	19
19	23	19	23	19	21	19	21	19	21	19	21	19	20	19	21	19	21	19	21	19	21	19	20
20	24	20	24	20	22	20	22	20	22	20	22	20	21	20	22	20	22	20	22	20	22	20	21
21	25	21	25	21	23	21	23	21	23	21	23	21	22	21	23	21	23	21	23	21	23	21	22
22	26	22	26	22	24	22	24	22	24	22	24	22	23	22	24	22	24	22	24	22	24	22	23
23	27	23	27	23	25	23	25	23	25	23	25	23	24	23	25	23	25	23	25	23	25	23	24
24	28	24	28	24	26	24	26	24	26	24	26	24	25	24	26	24	26	24	26	24	26	24	25
25	29	25	29	25	27	25	27	25	27	25	27	25	26	25	27	25	27	25	27	25	27	25	26
26	30	26	30	26	28	26	28	26	28	26	28	26	27	26	28	26	28	26	28	26	28	26	27
27	31	27	May 1	27	29	27	29	27	29	27	29	27	28	27	29	27	29	27	29	27	29	27	28
28	Apr 1	28	2	28	30	28	30	28	30	28	30	28	29	28	30	28	30	28	30	28	30	28	Mar 1
29	2	29	3	29	31	29	Jly 1	29	31	29	31	29	30	29	31	29	Dec 1	29	31	29	31	29	2
30	3			30	Jne 1	30	2	30	Aug 1	30	Sep 1	30	Oct 1	30	Nov 1	30	2	30	Jan 1	30	Feb 1	30	3
31	4			31	2			31	2			31	2	31	2			31	2			31	4

AFTER CARE

After the kittens are all safely born they should all be suckling or sleeping peacefully or crawling around quietly and the mother happily purring and she will now need all the rest she can get between the business of nestling and cleaning her kittens. Her licking also stimulates the actions of their bowels etc., and she keeps the kittens clean and cosy curling her body around all of them safely without ever lying on them, nor does she ever leave one outside the cosy circle.

All that is necessary for **the first two days** is to provide as much Lactol as she will take. The Lactol should be freshly mixed 2 or 3 times a day—the bowl being well cleaned out each time to prevent souring. Place the bowl close to her box and if the front of her box is low as advised on page 35, she will be able to step in and out without having to jump and will not hurt herself or the kittens.

The food and drink, as also the litter tray, should never be inside the nesting box—they may get knocked over—also being placed outside, they will encourage her to move around a little.

After the first 2 days some boiled fish such as cod or hake may be given, also some Lactol Biscuits, in addition to the bowls of Lactol. She will need plenty of milk-stimulating Lactol all the time and Lactol is given by many famous cat breeders because it contains the essential vitamins, proteins, fats, casein and albumin in easily digested form.

After the 4th day a little meat may be added to the diet but it should be noted that meat must not be given during the first 4 days.

Avoid any unnecessary handling of the kittens and do not expose them to any bright light. The mother will bring them out and into the light after about the 8th or 9th day when their eyes are open and at this stage, whilst the kittens are tiny, it is best to check the sexes. Later when the fur grows it is not so easy.

A healthy kitten is quiet and content, feeding regularly, sleeping, crawling or being washed by the mother—and feels warm to the touch. A sick kitten however feels cold and is noisy, possibly it is a weakling or may have a cleft palate and cannot suck properly. Watch whether it is feeding—there may be too many kittens for the mother, and the weakling will need to be put to sleep.

If all the kittens are noisy and feel cold, then the mother may have been undernourished during her pregnancy or she may have some ailment of the breasts but most cats can bring up 4 kittens and a really strong one can rear 5 or 6, but it must be remembered that she requires much more food than usual whilst nursing her young. The natural milk of small animals such as the mother cat and also the mother dog is much richer than cow's milk, that is why the special formulation of Lactol is a necessity for treasured and valued kittens, puppies and other small animals.

If the mother is short of milk give her extra Lactol as it stimulates the secretion of milk and at the same time give Sherley-Vite Tablets crumbled and mixed in with the Lactol, and let the meat given her be raw, provided this is after the 4th day. Supplementary feeds of Lactol may be given to the kittens if they seem to be undernourished.

Carefully examine the breast glands and teats from time to time as there may be a **blind teat** through which the milk cannot flow and the gland becomes swollen and painful. In such cases apply hot fomentations and try to squeeze out gently the contents of the gland through the teat—this is sometimes difficult, but with perseverance it generally comes after a time; if you fail to get the milk away an abscess generally forms, in which case continue the hot fomentations until the swelling is soft, when it should be freely punctured. This can safely be done with the point of a sharp clean and sterilized penknife—the wound must not be made too small or all the contents will not come away; afterwards gently squeeze out all the matter (pus) and thoroughly cleanse the wound with hot diluted Sherley's Antiseptic Lotion (a teaspoonful in a pint of hot water). Continue to wash the wound twice a day until healed. The diluted lotion is quite harmless to the kittens. See also Abscesses, Breast and Mammitis.

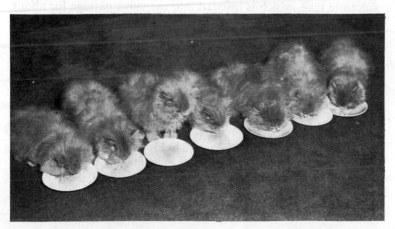

Whilst there is any soreness or inflammation of the breasts the mother may resent the kittens feeding from her and during such times temporary hand-feeding with Lactol can save the litter and maintain their normal rate of progress.

It is not practical to put a bandage round the cat whilst she is nursing, but it is advisable to see that she has clean cloths on her bed, and these should be changed daily. Sometimes one of the milk glands becomes hard, the result of the kittens not drawing off the milk from the particular gland.

The milk just seems to accumulate in the gland and at first it is not particularly painful, but if left the swollen gland increases in size and an abscess may form. Directly a gland gets hard rub it at once with equal parts of milk and warm water, and repeat this application twice a day.

After each application wipe off the superfluous fluid. As soon as the glands soften draw off the milk by gentle manipulation with the fingers. Whenever anything goes wrong with the milk glands, apply hot fomentations or bathe with water not too hot to burn and give the cat a dose of Lik-a-Med Laxative—it will not hurt the kittens.

Cats always have a certain amount of discharge for a time after the birth of the kittens, but normally it should cease by the time the kittens are 10 days old. If the discharge continues syringe twice a day with diluted Amplexol or Sherley's Antiseptic, a teaspoonful to ½ pint water and give Sherley-Vite Tablets. The best kind of syringe to use for a cat is an Enema Syringe with a vulcanite tube, which is inserted into the vulva passage for about three inches. The tube must be first well " Vaselined ". Give about 3 syringes full each time and the container should be held high, care being taken not to pump any air into the passage.

FEEDING INVALID CATS & KITTENS

The necessity may arise when, due to weakness, a queen might need to be hand-fed. The feeder illustrated opposite is actually the type used for premature infants and holds 6 teaspoonfuls of liquid. This is a valuable emergency item of equipment for breeders, being useful also for the supplementary feeding of invalid or backward kittens aged 3 or 4 weeks onwards.'

FEEDING BABY KITTENS

At 3 to 4 weeks old kittens will generally lap and should be encouraged to take a little Lactol. This is as good and as strong as the mother's milk, which is very much richer in fat than cow's milk. Lactol approaches more to the milk of a healthy queen than does any other food or preparation because it contains the essential vitamins, proteins, fats, casein and albumin—in easily digested form and, being manufactured under strict hygienic conditions it is free from harmful bacteria. Kittens cannot thrive so well when they are fed on cow's milk or other cheaper substitutes because they have to take far too much water and sugar, so often with troublesome results—indigestion, diarrhoea, distended stomach, etc.—often fatal. Lactol is used by most of the well-known cat and dog breeders.

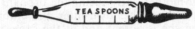

"Premature" Tube Feeder

The " Premature " Tube Feeder is graduated from one to six teaspoons, obtainable from Arnolds Veterinary Instruments Ltd., 54, Wigmore Street, London, W.1, costs 5s., plus 9d. postage and packing, and extra teats cost 5d. each; extra valves 7d. each.

Lactol is the only food necessary until the kittens are 3 or 4 weeks old when a little scraped lean raw meat or cooked fish may be given twice a day in addition to Lactol two or three times a day. See DIET.

HAND-REARING KITTENS FROM BIRTH

If the queen is unable to feed all or some of her kittens or if she dies when the kittens are born or before they are weaned and no foster-mother is available, they can be successfully reared by hand on Lactol. **During the first two weeks** of their life the Lactol should be diluted with four times its weight of water and must be given every two hours **day and night,** one drop at a time on the tongue, watching to see that it is swallowed before the next drop otherwise the kitten might choke.

A tiny medicine dropper or a fountain-pen filler is sometimes needed and very often, after a few days, the kittens are able to suck from the tiny teat end of the dropper (pierced with a small hole by using a red hot needle), or from a doil's feeding bottle. Hand-reared kittens usually lap much earlier than normally.

The quantity to be given should be not more than half a tea-spoonful during these first two weeks, after which the strength of the mixture and the quantity given are gradually increased and from two weeks onwards the feeding is from about 6 a.m. to midnight. Full details are printed on every Lactol tin.

FOSTER-MOTHER

As mentioned on page 32 most breeders of valuable pedigrees arrange a foster-mother in advance at the time of mating and sometimes a foster-mother needs to be found quickly in emerg-ency. (Many a nursing bitch and even wild animals which have lost their litters have suckled kittens and other orphan animals). It is however important first to smear the orphan kittens thor-oughly all over with some of the vaginal discharge and also the milk of the foster-mother, introducing the orphans one at a time by placing them amongst her own litter, preferably in complete darkness or when she is absent and at the same time gradually reducing her own litter. If however the mother refuses to accept them then a complete change-over of the litter might induce her to accept the orphans.

See also **Artificial Foster Mother,** page 32.

UNWANTED KITTENS

When the queen has a litter and the owner does not wish to keep all of the kittens, then at least one kitten, preferably a male, should be kept and the others destroyed immediately they are born. Keeping even one kitten will prevent much unhappiness to the mother and also, if all the kittens are destroyed, she may come into season again after only a few days. Then she will start " calling " and would need to be watched so that she does not have another litter quickly after the previous one as this could seriously affect her health.

If however, it is essential to destroy all of the litter then this must be done immediately each one is born so that none of them suckle at all. The queen should be given Sherley's Milk Suppression Tablets as soon as possible and if the teats look at all red and painful they should be bathed with cold water. Unless the milk glands are very swollen and painful the milk should **not** be drawn off as this would tend to stimulate and increase the milk secretion.

SEXING KITTENS

It is not so simple as one would imagine to distinguish the sexes of kittens, particularly in the long-haired breeds and especially when they are 8 or 9 weeks old. Many a complete female kitten has been purchased on impulse at a street corner or stall, where it may have been unscrupulously described as a " doctored tom " and has surprised the owner with a first litter after a few months.

Sexing is best undertaken when the kittens are quite small and when it is possible to distinguish their different colour markings and the details should be listed at the time for future reference when disposing of the kittens.

By comparing the kittens you will see the difference—
Hold the kitten in the palm of your hand, tail facing you and under the tail you will see two tiny openings.

In female kittens one day old, the space between the openings is only about $\frac{1}{4}$ inch.

In males the space between is about $\frac{1}{2}$ inch.

As they grow older so the space between increases and in adult females the space between is only about $\frac{1}{2}$ inch . . . the anus above and the vulva, a short slit, is below; whereas in adult males the space between is about $1\frac{1}{4}$ inches . . . the anus above and the tiny tip of the penis below. The complete male will have the two testicles in the space between. In the " doctored-tom " the testicles will have been removed.

After reading the details above it will be appreciated that when a kitten is two or three months old it can often be very difficult to differentiate between a doctored tom-cat and a female, therefore before choosing your kitten from a litter it is always a good plan to examine and compare the kittens underneath the tail as well as for general appearance.

STERILITY AND FALSE PREGNANCY

Sterility is not common in cats, but it does occur occasionally in both sexes, and particularly with the **males.** The cat may have been a successful sire for a season or more when, although he may continue to give the usual attention to the queens, he is no longer a successful sire, without any apparent reason. In such cases a raw meat diet is useful, as it also is with the queens who occasionally miss having kittens. Sterility also occurs occasionally as the result of too much stud work, the tom refusing to take

45

any notice of the queens, and in such cases the best thing to do is to give the tom a month's rest.

Stud cats need to have special feeding and the additional vitamins and essential minerals in the form of Sherley-Vite Tablets and also a course of Lintox Tonic for a few days each alternate week, especially if the cat is a poor feeder and gets low in condition and infertile due to too frequent stud. See also Stud Cats.

Sterility in females. Sometimes a queen does not come into season properly and in rare instances never comes on heat. This may be due to (1) having been mated by too young a male from which the sperm may be inadequate or immature and does not fertilise or (2) mated by a male which has become temporarily or permanently infertile because of too frequent stud.

In such cases it sometimes occurs that the female may have what is called a **false pregnancy** . . . she develops as if " in kitten ", the breasts and tummy and her appetite increase going even so far as making a nest, but she fails to have a litter.

Frequently, infertility in female cats may be due to some internal disorder therefore Veterinary examination is always advisable in investigating the cause of sterility.

It may be that the mating itself was not a complete success, that is why stud owners allow two matings to take place, spread over two days.

If the queen cat does not come properly into season she will need to have the additional vitamins in Sherley-Vites daily. These contain the fertility vitamin E. Also give red meat two or three times weekly.

Cryptorchidism (failure of both the testicles to descend), which usually takes place when 3 to 4 months old, renders a male infertile. Males with only one testicle descended may be fertile, although uncertain at times. Cryptorchidism can be corrected by a surgical operation by your Veterinary Surgeon. See page 124.

NYMPHOMANIA (" Over-sex " in queens)

An almost perpetual desire to be mated and irritable temper in queens may be caused by some disease of the ovaries, and excessive sex desire is aggravated by the fact that in such cases the queen is usually sterile.

In many cases occasional doses of Sherley's Sedative Tablets might calm the cat adequately, otherwise veterinary examination is advised.

MISCARRIAGE (ABORTION)

It may happen that a queen may have been mated at an inconvenient time, perhaps you would be on holiday when the kittens would be due to arrive or for some particular reason the mating is undesirable. Any inexperienced treatment can endanger the life of the queen, therefore no time should be lost in taking her to the Vet. who can give her special injection treatments. After the injection she must be kept indoors for some days as she may keep on calling the males. The injection does tend to lengthen the season for a time therefore extra care must be taken to prevent re-mating.

Injections can be given to induce premature birth and if the kittens would in any event be destroyed at birth this is often desirable but the circumstances are best discussed with your Veterinary Surgeon.

48

CHAPTER III
Breeds and Points

Classification of Breeds and Varieties — Details of Points —
Colourings — Eyes — etc.

THE VARIOUS BREEDS – VARIETIES – COLOURS – TYPES
Etc.

For those wishing to have, and perhaps show, a particularly splendid pet, or to keep cats as a hobby, breeding and selling the kittens, combining both pleasure and, maybe, a little profit, there are forty pedigree varieties to choose from, divided into two main types:—the long-haired cats and the short-haired cats, the varieties being as follows:—

Long-haired

1. Black
2. White (Blue eyes)
3. White (Orange eyes)
4. Blue
5. Red Self
6. Cream
7. Smoke
8. Silver Tabby
9. Brown Tabby
10. Red Tabby
11. Chinchilla
12. Tortoiseshell
13. Tortoiseshell and white
14. Blue Cream
15. Colourpoint
16. Any other variety

Short-haired

1. Black
2. White (Blue eyes)
3. White (Orange eyes)
4. British Blue
5. Russian Blue
6. Cream
7. Silver Tabby
8. Brown Tabby
9. Red Tabby
10. Tortoiseshell
11. Tortoiseshell and white
12. Abyssinian
13. Red Abyssinian
14. Seal-pointed Siamese
15. Blue-pointed Siamese
16. Chocolate-pointed Siamese
17. Lilac-pointed Siamese
18. Manx
19. Any other colour
20. Brown Burmese
21. Blue Burmese
22. Blue Cream
23. Chestnut Brown Foreign
24. Any other variety

Of all these varieties, the Siamese with Seal points are one of the most popular breeds, but if anxious to exhibit and possibly win at the shows, the novice should seek advice before buying a kitten. At the end of this chapter information is given about cat clubs, the secretaries of which are only too pleased to help beginners. Of the long-haired varieties, the Blue Persian, closely followed by the Cream are much sought after.

Each recognised variety has a standard of perfection by which it may be assessed. The standard is set by the Governing Council of the Cat Fancy and is for 100 points allocated for the various characteristics, such as colour, markings, head, eyes, body shape, tail and condition—the allocation of points varying for the various breeds.

In the **LONG-HAIRS,** the fur should be long and flowing, silky in texture—not woolly—with a full ruff around the neck, and the tail should be short and full. The head should be round and broad, with small tufted ears. The eye colourings vary according to the variety, but the shape should always be large and round. The body should be low on the ground on short legs. In the self-coloured, the colour of the fur should be sound all over and the same down to the roots, and there should be no shadings or markings. The kittens may be born with faint tabby markings, which fade as the coat grows.

SELF-COLOURED LONG-HAIRS

BLACK. The coat should be jet black, with no rustiness or white hairs. Usually the dense black coat required is not seen until the cat is an adult, as the kittens have a rusty appearance when young, and it is often the kitten with the rustiest coat that becomes the cat with the deepest black fur. The eye colour may be copper or orange. Intensive grooming is needed for the black long hair before showing. Daily brushing with Coatacine will help to produce a shining coat.

WHITE. There are two varieties of this breed. One having orange eyes and the other deep blue, apart from this the standard required is the same. The orange-eyed variety is usually better typed, with shorter nose and neater ears. This is due to the fact that they may be produced by mating a white with a blue, a black or even a cream, as this will still produce the orange eye colouring required, while endeavours to improve the type of the blue-eyed whites with another colour often results in the loss of the blue eye colouring. The white coat must be pure in colour, with no black hairs and no trace of yellow. There are two schools of thought regarding the preparation of white for showing—one believing in bathing and the other in powdering only. Bathing requires great care so that the animal will not catch cold afterwards. This is dealt with more fully on pages 24 and 61.

CREAM. The very attractive Cream long-hair should have a coat the colour of pale Devonshire cream, even all over right through to the roots—the tummy should not be paler than the rest of the body, and there must not be a white tip to the tail. A bad fault is a reddish line along the back referred to as ' hot '. The eye colour is required to be deep copper.

BLUE. With neat ears, a round broad head, deep orange or copper eyes, a long silky blue coat, short full tail, and a low stocky body, the Blue Persian is a fine example of what to look for when choosing or endeavouring to choose a long-hair that will come close to the standard required by the Governing Council of the Cat Fancy. It is one of the most if not the most popular of the long-haired varieties. The blue may be any shade ranging from light to dark, but the coat must be of even colour throughout right down to the roots. Eyes deep orange or copper.

RED SELF. The deeper the red in colour the better, but this is a breed very rarely seen, as most cats shown as " Red self " (i.e. completely red coloured) do prove to have some markings or bars, and are really a form of the Red Tabby. The eyes should be deep copper.

SMOKE. The type is the same as for the other long-hairs, but a Smoke is very different to look at and most striking in appearance, the undercoat being white with the top coat shading to black. The head and face should be dense black set off by a pale silver ruff. The breed is very difficult to produce, but often a female smoke mated by a black may produce very good smokes. If a Blue Persian is used, a Blue smoke may result, with blue where black should be. The eyes should be deep orange or copper.

TABBY LONG-HAIRS. There are three colours in this variety all requiring the same general pattern of markings, which is most important. There should be delicate tabby markings on the face, giving the appearance of spectacles around the eyes, swirls on the cheeks, an " M " on the forehead, two stripes around the

51

chest, with a pattern of markings forming a butterfly on the shoulders with solid stripes on the sides, stripes on the legs, and rings around the tail.

BROWN TABBY. The ground colour may be warm sable and the markings black. A fault that often appears is a white chin and a white tip to the tail. This is a breed that fails sometimes in type and care should be taken to choose a stud with very good type. Brown tabby mated to brown tabby may produce very good kittens, but if the type is not good—i.e. with tall ears, long nose, and a rangy body—mating with a good black long-hair may help to improve this. Hazel or copper eyes.

SILVER TABBY. A very striking variety with a ground colour of pure silver with markings of dense black. The stripes should be distinct from the pale background coat and not intermingled, nor should there be any brindling. There must be no brown or fawn tinge to the coat. The eyes may be hazel or green.

RED TABBY. The pattern here is very important and should be of a deeper red than the background coat of deep red. There must be no white tip to the tail. The stomach colouring must be the same as the rest of the coat. It is not true to say that Red tabbies are always males—males do seem to predominate in this breed, but when red is mated to red both male and female kittens may result. Often when a tortoiseshell female is mated by a red tabby, any red kittens that result will be males. Orange or copper eyes.

CHINCHILLA. This variety differs from all other long-hairs in that the coat is ticked. The undercoat should be white, with the ends of each hair on the back, sides, head, and tail tipped black, giving a distinctive silver effect. The ticking must not be too heavy or appear as patches. The type is as for the other long-hairs, but the eyes may be a beautiful blue-green or emerald. There must be no sign of yellow on the long silky coat.

TORTOISESHELL. A beautiful patterned cat with a coat deep black, rich red and cream, well distributed in patches. The colours must be bright, distinct and not intermingling with each other. There should be no white or tabby markings. The eyes may be deep orange or copper. Tortoiseshells are invariably female, although an occasional male may appear, but this will be a non-breeder, and a " tortie " should be mated to a male of one of her coat colours in an endeavour to produce a kitten like herself. The eyes may be deep copper or orange.

TORTOISESHELL AND WHITE. Another strikingly beautiful cat with the tri-colour coat of the Tortoiseshell plus white on the chest, face, legs and feet. There should be no white hairs in the patches of colour—each patch should be quite separate from each other. As with the tortoiseshells, they also are invariably female, and not easy to breed.

BLUE-CREAM. Often of outstanding type, being bred from the Blue and Cream Long-hairs. They are invariably female, any male being sterile. Breeding from a Blue Cream can be very interesting, as dependent on whether a blue or cream male is used, cream male and female kittens, blue male and female kittens and blue-cream kittens may turn up in the litter. The coat should be of the two colours intermingled evenly and not in patches. There must be no reddish tinges. The eye colour may be orange or copper.

COLOUR POINTS. An outstanding variety produced by selective breeding, bearing the coat colouring of the Siamese, but having the type of a long-hair. The coat should be cream with the points, that is the face, legs and tail, being the colour of the points of a Siamese, either seal, blue or chocolate. A striking feature is the brilliant blue eyes.

ANY OTHER COLOUR LONG-HAIRED. These are cats with long-haired coats that do not conform to any of the recognised varieties. They may be the result of crossing one variety with another—a Blue with a Chinchilla—a black and white cat, or may be the start of a new breed not yet recognised. The eye colour naturally would vary according to the colour.

SHORT-HAIRS

There are two definite breeds of short-haired cats, the British and the Foreign, each with their separate colour variations. British and Foreign are just names given to the breeds, and does not mean that the Foreign breeds are from abroad and the British home-grown, but is entirely an indication of type. The British are square sturdy cats and the Foreign cats are distinguished by their slender outlines and fine bone.

BRITISH SHORT-HAIRS

The chief points to remember in obtaining a show specimen are the following:—Body to be well knit and powerful, showing good depth. Chest full and broad. Tail thick at base, rather short than long, tapering to a point. Legs of good substance. Feet well rounded. Head broad between ears, cheeks well developed, face and nose short. Ears small and round at tops, carried somewhat forward, and not large at base. Coat short and thick. Eyes round and well-opened. General condition hard, strong and muscular.

THE SELF-COLOURS

BLACK. The coat should be shining jet black, with no brown. There must be no patches of white, particularly under the chin. The eyes may be deep copper or orange.

WHITE. As in the long-hairs, there are now two varieties, varying only in eye colour. The coat should be of pure white with no yellow tinges. The eyes to be of very deep sapphire or of deep orange colour.

BRITISH BLUE. One of the most popular of the British varieties, and some wonderful specimens may be seen at the shows. The colour may range from light to medium blue, but the fur must be the same all over right down to the roots, and there must be no tabby or other markings or white hairs in the coat. The eyes should be large and full, copper, orange or yellow in colour.

CREAM. A very attractive short-haired cat, but exceedingly difficult to produce without some stripes or markings, and a good specimen is very rare. The colours must be a rich cream, with no hint of ginger or red. The eyes may be hazel or copper.

BLUE CREAM—as in the long-haired variety, a result of mating usually between a Blue and a Cream, or may be produced from a tortoiseshell. Invariably female, the two colours should be softly intermingled, without patching. The type is as for the other British cats. The eye colour may be copper, orange or yellow.

TABBIES

The pedigree short-haired tabbies are very distinctive cats if they have the correct pattern of markings, which is most important. The markings should form a butterfly on the shoulder—two necklaces on the chest—often referred to as Lord Mayor chains, swirls on the cheeks, spectacles around the eyes, and an " M " on the forehead. The legs should have bracelets and the tail should be ringed with stripes. There are three colours:—

BROWN TABBY. Should have background colour of rich sable, with contrasting dense black markings. The type is as for the other British cats, and the eyes may be orange, hazel, deep yellow or green.

SILVER TABBY. A very distinctive breed, with a coat of pure clear silver, and markings of dense black, not intermingling in any way. The stripes and markings should stand out clearly from the coat background. The round eyes may be green or hazel.

RED TABBY. The pattern of markings and type is as for the other tabbies, but the beautiful colouring should be of deep rich red, with the tabby pattern very dense and of a darker red. The eyes may be hazel or orange.

" TORTIES "

TORTOISESHELL. The type as for the other British cats, but the coat to be of black and red (light and dark merging into cream). The patches to be well-defined, no smudging of the colours or any tabby markings. It is important that the legs, feet, tail and ears should also be well patched. This breed is usually female and it is quite difficult to breed true. A bad fault in a tortoiseshell is the appearance of white hairs in the red and black patches. A black or the self-coloured male may be used for breeding. The eyes should be deep orange or copper.

TORTOISESHELL AND WHITE. The same points apply as for the tortoiseshell, with the addition of white. There must be no white hairs in the colour patches, and no blurring of colour. They are invariably females, and a self-coloured male should be chosen for breeding, but even so, it is rare for a " tortie-and-white " to produce kittens like herself.

FOREIGN SHORT-HAIRS

As stated earlier, the Foreign short-hairs are entirely different in outline to the British cats, having slim lithe bodies, long tapering tails and pointed heads with fine muzzles and with ears sharp, large and pointed in comparison with other breeds. Fine bone, dainty small feet, oriental shaped eyes are typical of the Foreign cats. They should not be fat, and should have fine close short coat. The colour, of course, varies with the different varieties.

SIAMESE

The most popular of the short-hairs, or indeed of all the recognised breeds, is the Siamese, with the various points colouring listed below. Classified as a Foreign variety, the standard calls for a medium-sized cat, slim legs, hind legs slightly higher than the front, the feet small and oval, tail long and tapering—a very slight kink at the end is permitted. A squint is not allowed.

SEAL-POINTED SIAMESE. The body colour to be cream turning into a pale warm fawn on the back. Mask, ears, feet and tail known as the points to be a dark seal brown —the eyes a brilliant deep blue. The coat to be glossy and close-lying.

BLUE-POINTED SIAMESE. A colour variety of the Siamese, the standard required being the same as for the Seal-points, but the body colour to be glacial white and the points blue, with the body colouring shading gradually into blue on the back. The eyes to be a clear bright vivid blue.

CHOCOLATE-POINTED SIAMESE. The standard is as for the Seal-point, except that the colour of the points should be that of milk chocolate, and the body colouring ivory. The eyes should be a bright vivid blue.

LILAC-POINTED SIAMESE. The standard as before, but the body colouring to be a frosty white, and the points a pinky frosty grey—eyes a bright vivid blue.

56

ABYSSINIANS

There are two varieties of Abyssinians, those with ruddy brown coats, ticked with black or dark brown, and those with red coats. A body of " foreign type " is required, of slender build, graceful in appearance, a long pointed head, and comparatively large sharp ears. The main difference between the Abyssinians and the other foreign varieties is the attractive ticking on the coat. Each hair has two or three bands of ticking of black or dark brown. It is important there should be no bars or other markings on the head, tail, face and chest. Another fault often found in this variety is a white chin. The standard for the two is identical, except for the colouring which, in the case of the **Brown,** should be a ruddy brown, ticked with black or dark brown bands, and in the **Red,** should be a rich copper red, doubly or trebly ticked with bands of darker colour. The eye colour may be green, yellow or hazel. Abyssinians are usually very intelligent and make most companionable pets.

BURMESE

THE BROWN AND THE BLUE. There are now these two varieties of Burmese—the **Brown** and the **Blue**—the standard points allowed for each variety is the same—the difference between the two being the coat colouring. A medium sized cat is required, with a long slender neck, slim legs, small oval feet, a dainty, slim, long body, and a long tapering tail. The head in both varieties should be a short wedge, with pricked ears, large and wide at the base. The eyes should be of oriental shape, almond and yellow in colour in the Brown, yellowish green in the Blue. The Brown Burmese should be a rich dark-seal brown in colour, with a faint impression only of darker points colouring. The Blue Burmese should be a bluish grey, darker on the back, the coat having a silvery sheen.

CHESTNUT-BROWN FOREIGN

Another of the Foreign varieties. A dainty fine-boned cat is required, with a coat of rich chestnut brown, glossy in appearance—the head should be long, with large pricked ears. The tail should be long and tapering, without a kink. The eyes should be slanting, oriental in shape and green in colour. There must be no tabby markings or any white hairs. The coat colour should be even all over, with no impression of points.

RUSSIAN BLUE. Included amongst any other Foreign variety the true Russian is now very rare in this country, as unfortunately breeders have cross-bred with other varieties in an endeavour to perfect the breed, often with disastrous results; markings, rings on the tail and so on are now found in many specimens. Breeders are now working hard to bring back a cat close to the standard required, that is, a long lithe cat, with fine bone, and a head with a flat and narrow skull. The coat texture should be different from all other cats, and should be very short, close and lustrous, with a silky sheen, medium to a dark shade of blue in colour, even throughout. The eyes should be a vivid green, rather wide apart, and oriental in shape. The large pointed ears should be thin, almost opaque, with very little fur.

ANY OTHER VARIETY—As in the Long-hairs, but with short coats. They may be British or Foreign in type. Any cat not conforming to one of the recognised short-haired breeds may be registered as " Any Other Variety ". The cat may be cross-bred, resulting in an unusual colouring, or may be a new breed " made " by selective breeding which the owners hope to have recognised.

MANX

Originating from the Isle of Man . . . distinctive from all other cats in that it has no tail at all—really, definitely, **no** tail—the Manx should have a hollow where the tail would start in other breeds, and if there is even the slightest suspicion of a tail—it is not a true specimen of a Manx cat. The type is very much as required for the British cats. They are a fascinating breed and daily growing in popularity. They are very intelligent and have a personality all of their own. In spite of having no tail to balance, they are good climbers.

The height of their hind-quarters, the hind legs being longer than the front, gives the cat its rabbity or hopping gait. The back should be short and the rump as round as an orange. Colour is not important —all variations being permitted, as well as the self-colours such as white. The short coat is required to be double, that is soft and open with a thick under-coat. The eye colour varies with the coat colour.

BLACK MANX KITTEN

CHAPTER IV
Showing

Introductory — Cat Fancy Clubs — Preparation — Grooming — Bathing — Show-day requirements — Sending Cats by Rail, Plane, Sea — Quarantine.

INTRODUCTORY NOTES ON SHOWS

To find out about the rendezvous of Cat Shows is sometimes difficult, but they are held in various parts of the U.K., the largest being in London. It is quite a good idea to start at a small show to get an idea of how your kitten or cat likes being shown. There are three types of Shows. **A Championship Show** where challenge certificates are given—a winner of three of such awards given by three different judges at three separate shows becomes a Champion; **Exemption Shows and Sanction Shows** also held under the jurisdiction of the Governing Council of the Cat Fancy. Challenge certificates are not given at the last two mentioned, but such shows give novices an excellent opportunity to show their cats and to find out what the judges think of them.

A stamped addressed envelope should be sent to the Secretary of the Governing Council of the Cat Fancy, for a list of the shows. There is no central building but any breeder or Veterinary Society will give you the address of the Secretary. Application should be made to the Show manager five to six weeks before the date given for the show. A schedule giving details of the classes, rules, and an entry form will be sent to you. Choose your classes with care, fill in the form correctly, and send to the Show Manager with the correct entry fees before the closing date. In due course, you will receive a numbered tally, and a " vetting-in " card, as each exhibit is thoroughly examined by a veterinary surgeon before being admitted to the show hall. Any cat showing the slightest signs of illness, having dirty ears or fleas in the coat, is turned down and the entry fees forfeited. Your cat should be inoculated against Infectious Feline Enteritis at least three weeks before the show.

PREPARATION

However high the standard of your cat from a show point of view, it is the preparation prior to exhibiting that will be the telling point when the time for judging comes, and the general condition will also play an important part. Do not wait until the last few days before the show to get your cat in order, although if Sherley-Vite Tablets have been given regularly, his condition will be sounder and your task correspondingly lighter. An occasional dose of Sherley's Roundworm Tablets for Cats or Sherley's Worming Cream, should be given, because no cat can be got into good condition if suffering from worms. The ears should be clean and free from canker and Sherley's Canker Powder should be applied 3 or 4 days before the Show, otherwise your cat may be constantly scratching.

GROOMING. For the long-haired varieties, it is necessary to start daily grooming as a kitten, even twice-daily grooming when changing the coat, but care must be taken not to over-groom to the extent of pulling out the long coat, particularly the ruff around the head. For the paler varieties Amplex Dusting Powder sprinkled right down into the roots of the hair and brushed and combed completely out, will remove most dirt and grease from the coat and leave the fur standing away from the body. The fur should be finished off by brushing towards the head. Coatacine will help to remove any grease marks.

BRAN BATHS. Some breeders give bran baths a few days prior to the show as follows:—

Place a small quantity of bran in the oven on clean paper, or a new tin. When the bran is warm—care being taken not to make it too hot or it will discolour—have ready a clean bowl or tub in which the cat can stand, and gently run the warm bran well into the fur. As it is not possible to heat a sufficient quantity at one time, as it cools very quickly, have ready a fresh lot to place in the oven, so that it can be warming while the first is being used.

Brush the bran well out of the fur with a soft brush and rub well with a clean warm towel. You will find that after this treatment your cat's coat will be soft, clean and silky.

For Black cats, both long-haired and short-haired, a daily hand-grooming, finishing off with a thorough polish with a good velvet cloth or chamois leather cloth, will put on a lovely gloss. A little Coatacine will also help the gloss.

BATHING. Some well-known exhibitors do believe in bathing their cats, particularly white and chinchillas. It should be done a day or two before the show to allow the coat time to get back  some of its natural grease and to lessen the chance of the cat catching cold in the warm atmosphere of the show hall. The cat should be sat in a large bowl or bath and the coat wetted all over with warm water— Amplex Liquid shampoo (for dogs and cats) is very beautiful used on a cat's fur, as it will remove all dirt and grease, leaving the coat soft and silky. A little should be rubbed in, then rinsed well out. This should be repeated and the coat thoroughly rinsed. Be careful not to get any of the lather into the cat's eyes and ears. Dry the coat carefully with a clean warm towel, and do not let the cat go out for some hours. Brush and comb afterwards in the usual way. See WASHING.

Even the short-haired cats need some show preparation. Combing through with a small-toothed comb should remove any dirt. Brushing or hard rubbing-down with the hands or a chamois leather should give the coat a good sheen.

The ears should be wiped out gently with a little cotton wool. The occasional use of Sherley's Canker powder will help to keep the ears clean and to cure and prevent any possible canker trouble. The eyes may need wiping with Sherley's Eye Lotion in the corners, as dirt and dust may collect there, particularly in the long-haired varieties.

SHOW DAY. The best food to give cats and kittens before showing is lean raw meat, although some exhibitors prefer not to feed at all if considerable travelling is involved, feeding at the show with special tit-bits after the judging is finished. It is not advisable to give milk or milky food before a show, but clean, fresh water to drink. This should always be available for all cats at all times and it should be changed if the water or dish becomes at all soiled. At full-day shows there is so much dust floating in the air that it is wise to change the water several times during the day.

Nearly all the large shows held are for one day only, so that you may prefer not to feed until your return home and provided that the distance is not too great you can take your exhibit up in the early morning and return the same night. Vetting usually takes place between 9 and 10 a.m. and most shows close about 6 p.m. If it is not possible to arrive on the morning of the show in time for the vetting, the larger shows make provision for penning overnight, the veterinary surgeon attending the evening before the show to examine any overnight arrivals. Cats may not be sent to a show unaccompanied, but must be taken to the show and penned by the owner or the owner's representative.

Take care to provide a proper-sized basket with a secure fastening, but at the same time quick and easy to undo, as when you arrive at the Show the Veterinary Surgeon who examines the exhibits has not the time to wait while numerous knots of string are being untied. Cats must be taken to the show in proper containers and are not allowed to be led in on leads or carried in the arms. Having had your cats passed as fit and well, you are allowed into the Hall and having found the pen with the number corresponding to the tally around your cat's neck, you pen him yourself. A good plan is to take with you a bottle of diluted Sherley's Antiseptic or Amplexol and a rag so that you can give the cage extra cleansing and disinfection before penning the cat.

A warm white woollen blanket and an adequate sized sanitary tin must be put into the pen, but nothing else is allowed whilst the judging is in progress. Peat moss is usually provided for the sanitary tins. The cat may be fed in the early afternoon if required and given a drink. If the weather is very cold hot water bottles are allowed as long as they are concealed under the blanket.

The exhibitors may watch the judging, often from a gallery, but are not, as at dog shows, allowed to hold their cats, each judge having a steward with him for this purpose. The judge goes to each pen, and the steward places the cat on a small table in front of the pen to examine the exhibit. Any cat that cannot be brought out of his pen for judging is usually disqualified. The award slips are pinned up on a board for all to see the results, and after the judging is over, the prize cards are put on the pens.

Nearly all the cat shows are held during the winter months, for it is then that the long-coated varieties are at their best. There is however one big Summer show held in London in July or August where all the youngsters make their bow to the world, and where you may dispose of your young stock to those desirous of obtaining specimens of merit for the forthcoming winter shows. Neuters are also shown at this Show.

Kittens may be shown in the classes set aside for them, up to the age of nine months, at all Shows.

If you intend to show your kitten it is an excellent plan to accustom it to being shut up in a wire pen for an hour or two daily, as if used to this, when at the show he will not feel frightened and strange, and will thus show himself off to greater advantage.

On returning from the Show, see that the cat is warm and comfortable for the night, as if left in the cold outside after the excitement and hot atmosphere of the Show he may contract a chill. A good plan is to give a saucerful of warm milk, with perhaps, a little whisky added, and a crumbled Sherley-Vite Tablet as a preventive against infection, as although the cat should have been injected against Infectious Feline Enteritis, there are still other illnesses which may be contracted if care is not taken. Never give a cat castor oil . . . to some it is almost a poison. When several cats are kept, do not let any coming from a Show mix with others on their return. It is a wise precaution to keep them apart for at least a week.

Cat-keeping is a most fascinating hobby and although there is very little profit in it, a little pocket money may be made sometimes. Blue long-haired kittens are very popular with the public and fetch a ready sale as pets. The Siamese are still as popular as ever, and there is quite a demand for the usual Manx. Cats may be advertised in the weekly paper " Fur & Feather " where notices of cat shows, etc. may often be found.

REGISTRATION

Every cat or kitten before being exhibited at any Show under the rules of the Governing Council of the Cat Fancy, unless entered only in the Neuter, Non-Premier, Litter and Household Pet classes, must have been entered in the Register kept by the Council.

Applications for registrations must be made to the appropriate Registrar . . . there are Registrars for Long- and Short-hairs and a separate Registrar for Siamese.

The editor of one of the Cat Magazines or one of the Veterinary Societies will be pleased to give you the name and address of the Secretary.

To register a cat without a prefix the cost is 4s. 0d. and with a prefix 3s. 6d. A prefix is a distinguishing name—always the same—which may be used by a breeder before the name of a cat and kitten which he is registering. Once such a prefix is granted by the Governing Council at a fee of £2. 2s. 0d., it may be used by that breeder only. Applications for the approval and granting of a prefix should be made to the Secretary of the Governing Council of the Cat Fancy.

Registration lasts for the life of a cat, but when a cat or kitten that has been registered is sold, it must be transferred to the new owner before being shown again. Transfer forms can be obtained from the Registrars, and the signatures of past and present owners must be given. A transfer cannot be given on a Registration Form. The fee for registration of a transfer is 3s. 6d. but the new owner cannot alter the name of the cat as given on the registration form in any way.

A copy of the rules of the Governing Council of the Cat Fancy may be obtained free of charge on application to the Secretary. Intending exhibitors should read them carefully, while exhibitors of some years' standing would be well advised to peruse occasionally the rules governing shows and showing, as each year they are added to or altered. A copy of these rules is automatically sent out with every Show schedule.

The Governing Council of the Cat Fancy also compiles and sells a very useful booklet " **List of Cats at Stud** " price 2s. 6d. This gives the names and addresses of breeders of all the recognised varieties who have male cats they are prepared to use as studs for visiting queens. The booklet gives details of such cats, pedigrees, etc., and the fees chargeable for such service.

When exporting cats abroad, some countries require Export Certificates. These may be obtained from the Registrars—the fees being 15s. to £1. 15. 0. according to the document required.

CAT CLUBS. There are a great many Cat Clubs situated all over the country to cater for the many cat-lovers and breeders. Many of these Clubs, e.g. the Blue Persian Cat Society and the Abyssinian Cat Club are for those interested in specific breeds. The National Cat Club and many others are for those interested in all cats. The various clubs usually guarantee classes at the Cat Shows, where members may compete for special trophies and prizes. Many clubs hold their own shows under the jurisdiction of the Governing Council of the Cat Fancy, the largest being that held by the National Cat Club in December usually at the Olympia, London. There close on a thousand cats, both pedigree and pet, compete for hundreds of pounds worth of trophies and prize money. It is not possible here to give the names and addresses of all the Secretaries of the Cat Clubs, but a list of these will be sent—cost 6d. on application to the Secretary of the Governing Council of the Cat Fancy, who will also advise anyone endeavouring to find a kitten of a particular breed.

(Note . . . prices are those applicable at time of printing).

SENDING CATS BY RAIL

Would-be exhibitors at cat shows should bear well in mind the fact that it is **not now possible to send a cat to a show unaccompanied.** For many years now—all cats travelling to a show must be taken there and penned by the owner or the owner's representative. The same thing applies to the return journey. If an exhibitor takes several cats, in all probability, they will have to travel in the guard's van, but any cat travelling by train has to be paid for, the amount depending on the weight of the cat plus basket, and the mileage involved. This can be quite an item when taking show costs into account.

For whatever reason a cat has to travel by rail, the container must be adequate in size, but not so large that the animal rolls around in it. A basket is both light and airy, but can be draughty, and should be either lined with some material inside or covered with brown paper some way up on the outside, being careful not to exclude all means of ventilation. A strong wooden box may be used, provided it is not too heavy. Containers made of plastic are not advised, but there are containers made of fibre glass which are very good. A blanket, plenty of newspaper, or pine shavings is recommended for the cat to sit on. Hay is not too good unless the source is known as it does sometimes appear to encourage fleas. **Do not give food for an hour or two before sending,** as the jolting of the train will often make a cat sick if it has been given food just before starting. The box or basket should have a handle on the top so that nothing else may be flat on it to exclude air or squash the container. " LIVE CAT " should be printed in very large letters on the top and on all sides of the box or basket. See TRAVEL SICKNESS.

SENDING CATS BY PLANE AND SEA

The regulations vary according to the Air or Steamship Line and the destination, therefore it is advisable to obtain all information well in advance. Except for short accompanied journeys a special box container, with vessels and trays for food, water, and toilet purposes, is necessary—and can be obtained through travel agencies. Such specially designed containers should be used for all unaccompanied journeys. The cat can then be fed and watered *en route* and all danger of escape is avoided. It is always a good plan to accustom the cat to the travelling box or some similar container during the week or so before the journey . . . starting with just a few minutes at intervals each day and gradually increasing the periods. The cat will need to be given Sherley's Sedative Tablets before, and if possible, during the journey.

The R.S.P.C.A. issue a leaflet on the subject entitled " Sickness and Fright in Dogs and Cats Travelling by Train, Car or Airplane," available from the R.S.P.C.A. on request.

QUARANTINE

With a view to preventing the introduction of rabies, the importation of certain animals including cats into Great Britain from abroad is controlled by the Ministry of Agriculture, Fisheries and Food, Whitehall Place, London, S.W.1. No cats may be landed without a licence previously obtained for them or through one of the various local offices of the Ministry. All such licences require the animals to undergo detention and isolation for six months on approved Veterinary premises. Imported cats must be conveyed from the port of entry to the place of detention by approved Carrying Agents. A list of Carrying Agents can be obtained from the Ministry.

Similar conditions are imposed by the Authorities concerned in Eire, Northern Ireland and the Channel Islands, whilst cats imported from abroad may not enter the Isle of Man until they have completed the requisite six months' quarantine in Great Britain, in Eire, or in Northern Ireland.

Provided that they are not actually subject to quarantine restrictions owing to their recent importation from abroad, cats may be moved freely between and within Great Britain, Northern Ireland, Eire, the Channel Islands, and the Isle of Man.

LONG-HAIRED TABBY

SHERLEY'S REMEDIES
for the control of
WORMS, INSECTS, PARASITES, &c.

ROUNDWORM TABLETS
Absolutely safe and effective.
No fasting . . . No purging.

TAPEWORM TABLETS
For adult cats—A single dose clears
Tapeworms.

New—pleasantly flavoured—So easy to give
SHERLEY'S WORMING CREAM
For Dogs & Puppies, Cats & Kittens
Effective for ROUNDWORMS, THREADWORMS,
HOOKWORMS (Uncinaria) & NODULAR WORMS
All Sherley's Worming Remedies are safe and effective,
and there is no fasting—no purging

"VAMOOSE" PET POWDER
Safe for all your pets.
Handy puffer tin, or drum.
Kills insects and parasites.

"NO-SCRATCH" PUFFER
Quickly stops scratching.
Kills insects, parasites
and fungus too.

CANKER LOTION
In easy to use capsules.
Specially for dry Canker.
Soothing and effective.

CANKER POWDER
Quickly clears wet canker.
In easy to use puffer.
Prevents recurrence.

SHERLEY'S INSECTICIDAL DOG SHAMPOO
EQUALLY SAFE FOR CATS & KITTENS
A scientific blend of gentle liquid cleansing ingredients. Combined with most
efficient harmless insecticides

CHAPTER V
Parasites

Prevention — Coccidiosis — Fleas — Lice & Nits — Harvest Mites (Chiggers) — Maggots — Notoedric (Sarcoptic) Mange — Otodectic (Ear) Mange Mite — Ringworm — Ticks — Worms (Roundworm, Hookworm, Tapeworm, etc.)

PREVENTION IS BEST

Parasites include insects in their various stages of development, and plant life, etc., living in or on an animal. In cats, which have such sharp claws, because of self-inflicted wounds in their efforts to relieve the irritation, they can cause a great deal of suffering, loss of strength and other complications. A cat troubled with parasites cannot hope to be anywhere near perfect. With early and correct treatment however most parasites are relatively easy to control and exterminate with safety—and in fact regular preventive treatment with Sherley's Preparations can keep your cat free from most parasites.

It should be borne in mind that **parasites or their eggs or larvae can lie dormant amongst bedding, carpets, floorboards, skirtings, cracks, etc. for days, weeks and in some cases months . . . and the cat can be reinfested repeatedly at intervals** . . . therefore even after the condition appears to be well and truly cleared, preventive applications at regular intervals are strongly recommended.

A healthy and well-cared-for cat keeps itself scrupulously clean but if you see your cat scratching or biting itself or repeatedly shaking and scratching its head make an immediate careful examination to ascertain the cause of the irritation. Many of the parasites can cause skin sores through the scratching and biting . . . others are eaten and cause worm infection . . . others affect the general health by sucking the blood.

Some parasites can even spread infestation and skin disease and serious internal diseases to children and other members of the family.

If there are any signs of canker in the ear, or eczema or mange on the face or body, treat the condition without delay, thus reducing the length of treatment required to control the infection.

Parasites can change the health, temper and appearance of the most beautiful and docile cat if the infestation is not quickly controlled . . . " PREVENTION IS BETTER THAN CURE ".

The part where a cat scratches itself can be misleading and it is not always an indication of the infected part. Sometimes it is nerve reaction from a position it cannot reach . . . watch where it nibbles at the skin, this is usually nearer the spot.

Applications of insecticides etc., are best done out-of-doors, or, if the cat has been so trained when a kitten it can be treated and then placed in a sail-cloth bag with drawstring top (like a " duffle" bag), closed around the neck to keep him from scratching or licking off the insecticide, or escaping. After about 10 to 20 minutes he can be released and excess powder must then be brushed out. See page 14.

COCCIDIOSIS

(Pronounced Cock-sidi-osis)

This is caused by microscopic parasitic bacteria or organisms (Coccidia) and there is a great variety of species. The organisms can be consumed by the cat when " worrying " infected wild rabbits, mice, or on ground where chicken runs have been, etc., and they are also often fly-borne, flies settling on excreta and then on food dishes. The coccidia multiply enormously in the stomach and intestines—resulting in a form of illness similar to dysentery in humans.

Symptoms. Kittens are more severely affected than adult cats. The stools are watery, sometimes bloodstained, and the cat becomes thin, weak and loses appetite, eyes discharging pus, and usually a high temperature. Kittens can become infected from the mother although if still suckling they do seem to be less severely affected, perhaps acquiring some immunity from the mother's milk.

Kittens or cats can be infected by walking about on infected stools then licking their feet clean and because of the great variety of species of Coccidia, although immune to one particular type after such illness, the animal may still be subject to similar infections and symptoms, from other types of coccidia.

Prevention. This disease is usually created by unclean conditions, lack of attention to hygiene, or just thoughtlessness on the part of the owner. All food and drinking utensils should be cleaned, scrubbed and rinsed out daily. Never leave " left-overs " of food to be eaten later unless properly covered to exclude flies. Excreta should be removed immediately, newspapers destroyed—preferably burned, litter pans cleaned out and changed daily and sprayed with a good disinfectant such as Amplexol or Sherley's Kennel Fluid or Antiseptic Lotion.

Every precaution should be taken to be sure that flies do not settle and carry infection to food and drink and where several cats and kittens come together, as in a cattery or pet shop, then extra special hygienic precautions are absolutely essential. Even an owner can spread infection from shoes or after handling an infected cat or kitten. Therefore, where numbers of cats and kittens are kept, disinfection of hands and shoes, is advised—for the feet, a mat or sack sprinkled each day with diluted disinfectant as above, is a worthwhile safeguard.

Treatment. If your kitten is young and he has a high temperature (above 103°F=39.4°C. or more) with the symptoms described above then your Veterinary Surgeon should be consulted and he will be able to confirm by microscope examination of the kitten's droppings whether the illness is coccidiosis because this will be saturated with myriads of the minute organisms.

Diet. In coccidiosis it is important to give food rich in fat . . . Lactol contains three times as much fat in easily digested form as cow's milk and is therefore the perfect drink and in fact, cats and kittens fed on Lactol are far less subject to coccidiosis infection.

This particular infection should improve within a few days, otherwise, if the patient becomes worse consult a Veterinary Surgeon in case there may be other complications. (See also Diarrhoea and Enteritis).

FLEAS

Fleas are a source of great trouble to cats, the irritation of the flea-bites causing the cat to scratch itself incessantly, often with severe self-inflicted wounds and sores. **Furthermore, fleas are carriers of the adult-cat tapeworm and diseases,** and they also affect the general health and condition of the cat.

There are several species . . . human fleas, dog fleas, cat fleas, etc., which generally prefer to keep to their natural hosts but contrary to general belief the cat flea will live on other animals and also will bite humans if hungry. Your cat may pick up fleas from other cats or from nosing around where there have been wild rabbits, hedgehogs, etc.

The flea alights on the body of the cat and stays there until it has sucked enough blood to satisfy it, then it usually hides away in cracks and corners, between floor boards and skirtings, behind stoves, between stones, etc. Here the female makes a nest and lays its eggs, which may lie dormant for days or in winter for weeks or months, until the atmosphere is warm and damp, when the eggs hatch out into the larvae (worm) stage so that your cat can be repeatedly infested from his own home surrounding. Later more baby fleas develop and climb up the cracks and wait to jump upon a suitable host, perhaps again on your cat and stay there biting until their hunger is satisfied, usually a day or two.

The fleas extract blood and serum and into the bites inject a very irritating substance which prevents the blood clotting and so enables them to suck out as much blood as they need without difficulty. The tiny flea-bites irritate so intensely that an animal like a cat with sharp claws can damage itself quite badly in its attempts to relieve the itchings. Fleas are often very difficult to find . . . when looking for them they move away quickly as searching fingers disturb the fur—they do not jump as human fleas do. Their excreta can be seen like flecks of ash when the fingers are rubbed against the lie of the coat.

It is comforting to know that fleas can be quickly exterminated with Vamoose Pet Powder or Sherley's No-Scratch. One dusting will clear the adult fleas in a matter of minutes and further dustings at fortnightly intervals will prevent reinfestation. All bedding, rugs, boards, etc., need to be treated each time. Treatment of movable items is best carried out in the garden so that the fleas do not hop off onto carpets and floor crevices and hide there to breed or find their way back to the cat. If the cat continues to scratch look for some other cause on or near the part he keeps scratching. (See also notes on Bathing).

Never use any insecticides which contain D.D.T.

Many household insecticides and sprays are harmful to animals.

In tropical areas other types of fleas are found infesting humans, wild and domestic animals. The " JIGGER " and the " STICK-TIGHT " are widespread in some areas and in some infestations need specialised treatments.

LICE (& NITS)

Although lice are not usually found on cats living under normal conditions, those in dirty premises or on farms or scavenging in dustbins or long-haired cats with matted neglected coats can be troubled with lice—and can pass them on to other cats by contact —or by scratching themselves they shed lice and eggs and so spread infestation. The eggs can survive away from the host for months until conditions for hatching are favourable, e.g. after lying dormant through the whole winter. Cats which do not bother to clean themselves sometimes collect lice around and under the tail.

There are various types of lice—those on cats are usually greyish-yellow, smaller in size than fleas, and without wings. They are found mostly around the neck and live their whole lives on the host—some types sucking the blood other types living on skin scurf and debris—the female laying eggs (nits), 100 or more a month, each of which she " glues " on to a hair.

Lice can be so damaging as to cause anaemia from loss of blood and the irritation causes the cat to scratch repeatedly, resulting in injuries and sores. In cats and kittens lice can endanger the whole litter, the skin of the kittens acquires a leathery feel and they become terribly thin and weak.

Checking for lice and nits . . . push the hair " against the grain " to reveal the skin and the lice appear as a colony of small greyish specks. Under a magnifying glass they can be seen to be moving. The nits are yellowish-grey specks stuck to the hairs.

Treatment . . . In previous times it was extremely difficult to get rid of lice and even more difficult to exterminate the nits, but nowadays with Sherley's Vamoose Pet Powder or No-Scratch, two or three dressings at intervals of one week will get rid of the lice and nits in all stages of their development. The repeat treatments are necessary to exterminate any nits which may have survived and hatched out. As with other parasites prevention is the best cure—occasional treatments of the cat and other pets, also bedding, baskets, etc., is advised.

The Sherley's Pet Insecticides should be worked thoroughly into the roots of the hair, particularly where the lice are found and then any excess of powder should be well brushed out. After any lice infestation your pet will be very " run down " and will benefit enormously from a daily Sherley-Vite Tablet.

HARVEST MITES (CHIGGERS)

It is only the tiny larval stage of the Red Bug which is picked up by cats and dogs in the country and in gardens and they are very difficult to see and recognise on many cats because they are so tiny. They are red in colour and appear like grains of red sand. They burrow into the skin and inject an intensely irritating substance which keeps the blood from clotting and suck out blood, causing small red inflamed patches, each with a centre spot. After having gorged themselves on blood for a few days they drop off and pass on to the next stage of their development and are then not troublesome to cats.

The spots are extremely irritating and as they are very often numerous the condition of the skin can be mystifying as there would seem to be no particular cause and therefore eczema or some mange condition is suspected. The red sandy-like larvae can be identified in scrapings from the skin inspected under a strong magnifying glass. The extreme irritation causes the cat to scratch itself, inflicting further skin damage.

Treatment and the control of re-infestations are the same as for lice, with regular fortnightly applications of Vamoose Pet Powder during the summer when the grass is tall around the fields and roadsides.

MAGGOTS

Cats occasionally get maggots (the larval stage of the blow-flies) through blow-fly eggs being laid on the skin around bites and sores that may not be observed by the owner owing to the thick covering of the cat's fur. Not until the maggots are observed crawling around the area does one become aware of their existence. Here again a little application of Sherley's No-Scratch powder will destroy these maggots and they can then gently be removed with forceps and the underlying raw place or wound washed with Antiseptic Lotion then dressed with Eczema Lotion or Ointment.

MANGE (NOTOEDRIC & SARCOPTIC)—SCABIES

The **Notoedres cati** and the **Sarcoptic scabeii** are similar mange parasites, microscopic in size and hardly visible to the naked eye. The former, somewhat the smaller, usually lives on cats, the latter mainly on dogs, **but both types are contagious to other animals and to people** (see below) by direct contact and even from mange mites picked up from the ground or other indirect contact. On the animal they prefer warm areas such as between the chest and elbows and inside the thighs.

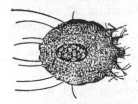

Sarcoptic, or Common Mange Parasite
(Magnified 50 times)

Specimens may be seen by examining, under a microscope, scrapings taken from the skin of a cat or dog suffering from Mange.

The female of the mange parasite burrows in under the skin of the cat and lives there laying its eggs, 20 or 30 or more at a time, at intervals, and the eggs hatch out in about 7 days and this process goes on and on so that multiplication of the parasites can be at a terrific rate. Meanwhile, the males and intermediate larvae and nymph stages live on the skin surface and in the sores which are created.

In its early stages mange differs little from ordinary eczema and there are the usual first indications of any skin trouble, the incessant scratching and rubbing. Mange is often mistaken for ordinary eczema but mange is contagious whereas eczema is not, therefore if only one animal is infected then the trouble is most likely eczema; on the other hand, if more are infected then it is probably mange. In mange there are tiny sores and the hair comes out in patches, at first around the head and front legs and subsequently anywhere on the body. Scabs and sores form, the fur becomes thin and broken and the itching causes the cat to scratch itself, thus causing more sores and wounds. If the condition is neglected the skin becomes hard and dry, the cat terribly thin and anaemic, with a nasty mousy smell, and would eventually die.

When the mange mite affects humans, fair haired people seem more likely to get the infection. It is usually confined to the wrists, and can set up great irritation, particularly in bed, the warmth stimulating the parasite to activity. Where the bad habit exists of sharing one's bed with the cat or the dog, then a rash may spread all over the person's body and it is advisable to consult a doctor. Clothing may be infected, particularly in the region of the cuffs and sleeves of jackets, and should be dealt with by spraying them with " Vamoose " Pet Powder and leaving for a day—then thoroughly brushing out and having the garments washed or dry-cleaned. Owners having a rash of this nature can be a source of later infection to pets belonging to their friends.

Treatment . . . The cat may have thousands of the parasites on its body and will roll around on carpets and scratch itself incessantly, spreading infection everywhere, therefore affected cats should, if possible, be isolated from other animals for thorough treatment . . . and all animals and furniture need to be treated to prevent the spread of infestation. The mange parasites can be readily identified by a Veterinary Surgeon from skin scrapings, although nowadays early prevention is simplified thanks to the special formula of Sherley's No-Scratch Powder which includes ingredients to clear and control and also to prevent re-infestations of the mange parasites—provided the cats or other pet animals have not been too long neglected.

Treatment is indeed simple now in normal household conditions but because these parasites can still live away from an animal or person for about a fortnight, all bedding, carpets, upholstery, baskets, floorboards or skirtings, etc., in fact everywhere the cat lives, eats and sleeps, will need repeated treatments to **prevent re-infestation**. Any boxes or cloths which are of no value should be burned . . . woodwork and carpets well sprinkled with Sherley's No-Scratch or Vamoose Pet Powder and brushed into cracks and crevices overnight and the surplus brushed away in the morning, or after an hour or two if necessary.

The cat itself is sprinkled with the powder and the surplus powder and scurf etc., brushed out on newspaper after about 15 to 20 minutes. All brushings and dust should be burned immediately. (See also note on page 70 re " duffle-bag ").

The treatment needs to be repeated at intervals . . . on the cat itself every 4 days for a fortnight to kill off any eggs which may hatch out . . . **furniture, floors, etc., every 10 days for 3 to 4 weeks. In Catteries, the timber and metal parts can be sterilised by lightly applying a blowlamp.**

Be sure to brush away all surplus powder as the cat will lick itself and licking too much of the powder could cause tummy upset.

In mild climates cats are not usually affected by the Demodectic Mange Parasite which affects dogs (also known as Follicular or Red Mange). Any red sores appearing around the eyes and face should be treated with Sherley's Eczema and Mange Lotion.

OTODECTIC (EAR) MANGE MITES

The term " Canker of the Ear " is used very widely to describe a number of different ailments inside the ear but in this chapter we are dealing only with the Otodectic (Ear) Mange Mite.

This parasite is a very tiny mite and is perhaps the most common original cause of all forms of ear canker. It lives and breeds within the ear canal, in a crumbly secretion, cream to brown coloured, and in this the females lay their eggs every ten to fourteen days. The eggs hatch out in about 7 to 10 days, thus multiplication is almost continuous. Under a strong glass the mites can be observed moving about in particles of the secretion.

The mites set up intense irritation within the ear, the cat shaking its head and frequently scratching, causing sores and bare patches often about the size of a sixpence, behind and on the ears. Also, the head-shaking spreads particles of the secretion and its contents on the cat's face and bedding, which can cause later re-infestation after the ears have healed.

If correct treatment is neglected, then due to the frequent scratchings, inflammation and painful sores follow, often with odorous discharge. The cat itself may become rather pitiful . . . shaking its head and scratching . . . and if too painful to scratch, will walk with its head held on one side . . . changing entirely in health and temper, reticent and resenting any attempt to stroke its head . . . giddiness attacks, falling down, getting up, walking on a few paces and falling again . . . noises in the head . . . and deafness.

Early treatment is essential. Apply Sherley's Canker **Lotion** twice daily until the irritation has ceased, then occasional treatments at intervals of about 10 days, followed by regular use of Sherley's Canker **Powder** fortnightly to prevent new infections.

Any sore or bare patches on the outside flaps of the ears or on the head should be treated with Sherley's Veterinary Ointment and they will quickly heal and will then grow new hair. See also Cysts (Haematoma).

To ensure that the medicaments reach the affected surfaces, if there is any wet mattery discharge this should be wiped away with dry cotton wool and any crusted wax or discharge cleansed with a solution of equal parts of Methylated Spirits and warm water, then dried with fresh wool. Inside the ear one can use a match stick with cotton-wool wound around the tip, but do not poke around inside the inner ear. Always burn used wool and scrub hands thoroughly, immediately. See also CANKER, page 120.

RINGWORM

Ringworm is a very contagious vegetable fungus disease, often very difficult to recognise with the unaided eye in cats and dogs because it so often fails to develop typical rings on the skin. In some types of ringworm there is very little irritation . . . in other types there is irritation but so little to see that there seems to be no apparent cause for the cat scratching itself. The disease therefore often passes unnoticed or untreated and cats can carry the disease under the skin and spread the fungus every time they scratch or rub themselves, for months or years.

Ringworm is very contagious to humans, particularly to children and others who frequently fondle their pet cat, and the diagnosis of Ringworm often comes by the round-about route of owner or child being infected and leading them to suspect the cat as the source. In the same way a human infected can pass ringworm on to another pet.

In moderate climates the most common type of ringworm in cats and dogs is the Microsporum Canis spread from mice and rats living in dark damp holes and corners but ringworm is also windborne and after an infected animal scratches itself the spores can be windswept for miles and can spread rapidly, or can lie dormant for a considerable time, so that even a pet which is most carefully guarded can become infected without any apparent contact.

When a cat mauls an infected mouse the infection on the cat normally appears first around the lips, nose and claws and can spread by degrees around the face and head and then the paws simply by the cat resting its head on its feet. An infected tom cat can pass infection to females and thence to litters and in the young kittens the disease can have very drastic results.

Ringworm affects young animals and young children more severely than adults, perhaps resistance is later acquired by adults . . . and there may be some vitamin deficiency . . . weaker kittens in a litter can be much more susceptible to the effects of the disease than the larger stronger kittens and cats can go through their whole lives, from kittenhood onwards, carrying the infection.

On the skin of the adult cat the condition varies because there are so many different types of fungus infections. The areas of ringworm may be tiny (from pinhead size) up to about the size of a shilling, round or mis-shapen oval patches, thick crusty patches with depressions in the centre or red and inflamed, or just small patches of a greyish ash-like powder . . . hairs may be encrusted together near the base and broken off leaving stubby patches.

Ringworm also grows in the hair roots and on the hairs themselves and at the **roots of the claws too,** where it appears as a thin crescent shaped crusty scab.

Diagnosis is difficult or delayed for the reasons mentioned above but if ringworm is suspected search the skin for bare or stubby patches or for crusts or for small patches of ash-like powder. The Veterinary Surgeon can confirm the disease by taking scrapings of the skin and hairs for examination under a microscope or Wood's Glass. In the latter the examination is made under Ultra-Violet light when the infection shows up in luminous form.

Where ringworm exists or is suspected to exist the cat (and other pet animals) should be treated first with Sherley's No-Scratch and if necessary examined by the Vet., and the owner likewise should consult his doctor.

Do not forget to institute a campaign against rats and mice. " Defest " Warfarin is the safest and most efficient modern rodenticide and the safety precautions to avoid pets taking the " Defest " are stated on the package.

TICKS (from Sheep and Cattle)

The ticks that in summertime are active on and depend normally on sheep and cattle for their food, which they acquire by sucking the blood of their host, also occasionally infest cats.

At a certain stage of their life history, after hatching, the ticks, just visible to the eye, congregate on the stems of long grasses. Any cat brushing his way through such infested herbage can " hook " a number of these larval ticks which are waiting for such a victim, and they promptly attach themselves to the skin and commence sucking their host's blood. In doing so they begin to swell enormously, and within a few days attain the size of a small bean and when fully gorged they release their hold on the skin and drop off, the females then laying their eggs in crevices on the ground.

The body of a tick is little more than a bag of blood, purple in appearance, and its head and feet are not visible when it is in situ. If it is rubbed off by the cat or pulled off by force by human intervention, then the sucking apparatus and head of the tick are left embedded in the cat's skin. Acting as a foreign body with considerable irritant properties, the buried headpiece sets up a nasty festering sore, so **it is important that the tick be got rid of all in one piece. The tick may be painted with chloroform, or with methylated spirit at the junction of the body with the embedded head when it releases its hold and can be drawn away complete with tweezers gently applied at its head end.** Applications of neat Sherley's Antiseptic Lotion, well rubbed in and left on for ten minutes will often release the majority of the ticks which can be then gently picked off with the tweezers complete with the head. All ticks removed should be burned.

A weekly application of Sherley's No-Scratch, well dusted into the skin and then the surplus well brushed out, does much to help prevent infestations . . . also bathing with Sherley's Medicated Shampoo after removal of the embedded ticks with forceps, will help to heal the skin.

(Remember . . . NEVER use any D.D.T. Insecticides on animals.)

WORMS

Worms of numerous types have infested cats for thousands of years. In wild animals they usually cause little or no disturbance of health, but under conditions of domestication worms are able to build up their numbers and can cause serious loss of condition and even illness. A cat or kitten with worms will have an unusually large and ravenous appetite but will appear thin and out of condition and ill, in spite of extra feeding or conditioning.

Extracts from The Lancet 20-6-64 p.p. 1357 and 1359 (*italics added*)
" Toxocara canis, the common canine roundworm, matures in the puppy's *or kitten's* gut producing ova that contaminate the soil. If the child eats this soil, the ingested ova hatch in the upper-bowel and the larvae bore through the gut wall into blood-vessels and lymphatics to spread throughout the body . . . the puppy *or kitten* infected with toxocara roundworm is no companion for the child. Regular deworming is strongly recommended for all puppies and breeding bitches and kittens *and breeding queens* . . . "

The medicaments for Roundworms and for Tapeworms are completely different and the treatments are therefore entirely separate.

ROUNDWORMS	TAPEWORMS

These infest kittens, causing tummy upset and illness. Most adult cats are infected but are resistant to the effects of roundworms.

All pregnant queens must be treated a fortnight after mating or up to 3 weeks before kittening otherwise the eggs in their milk pass on to the litter.

All kittens must be treated at 6 weeks of age, and again a fortnight later to exterminate any larvae since hatched out.

These infest adult cats, causing ravenous appetite with thin and ill appearance because the tapeworms rob the cat of the nourishment in his food.

If left untreated, the tapeworms multiply enormously.

The cat quickly becomes emaciated and poor looking with variable appetite and may suffer from gastritis, constipation, diarrhoea, convulsions at intervals — progressively becoming completely ill.

Roundworms—in the motions or vomited appear like round pieces of cotton or thin string . . . yellow or grey or pink colour . . . pointed at both ends. Length ½″ up to about 6″.

Tapeworms appear in the motions or crusted under the tail into segments like small seeds. White or greyish-white colour, and seem to contract and expand.

ROUNDWORMS

Whilst roundworms usually infest grown cats they are not serious in adults, but in kittens they are responsible for a variety of harmful conditions such as **pre-disposition to rickets, anaemia, indigestion, under-nourishment and lowering the resistance to infectious diseases.**

If the queen is infected and has not been treated after mating her milk contains the eggs of the worms which proceed to develop

in the stomach and bowels of the kittens from birth and begin to reveal their presence when the kittens are about 6 to 8 weeks old when starting to take food other than the milk of the queen.

Where several cats are kept and litters are bred then all the adult cats used for breeding should be treated for roundworms twice a year.

Good mousers particularly, suffer from roundworms all their lives and occasionally the roundworms set up a great deal of inflammation in the stomach and bowel. In such cases Sherley's Gastrine Tablets should be given from time to time.

Strong, healthy, properly fed kittens may have quantities of worms without obvious signs at first, but naturally they retard the kitten's progress. The presence of roundworms affects the coat, which may be rough instead of smooth and silky, the body thin yet with a pot-belly, bad breath, big appetite at times but at other times little inclination to eat, and often the third eyelid (the Haw) is visible.

To ensure a good start in life all kittens should be dosed for worms, whether they are apparent or not, at the age of six weeks, or even a week earlier if it is obvious that worms are present and are having a harmful effect. At this tender age strong medicine is liable to bring convulsions, resulting in death; therefore, use only Sherley's Roundworm Tablets or Worming Cream—they are efficient and absolutely safe.

It is also advisable to repeat the dose a fortnight later, since larval forms of the worms may be present outside the stomach and bowels and these continue to migrate into the bowel after the clearance effected by the first dose. This second dose ensures the extermination of such secondary infestation and unless the second dose is given, the effectiveness of the remedy might well be in question, when worms re-appear in this manner.

Sherley's Roundworm Tablets may be given with absolute safety and there is no need for any preliminary fasting or purging, although a small dose of Lik-a-Med Cream Laxative given the evening before worming helps to give more concentrated clearance of the roundworms by relieving the bowels before medication. Do not use any worming medicines at all on cats or kittens which are very ill with Cat Distemper or Infectious Enteritis, etc., or if there is a high temperature. Worming is best left until the animal is reasonably well.

HOOKWORM (Uncinaria)

There are various types of Hookworms, but in moderate climates it is only the species **Uncinaria** which may be troublesome to cats and dogs, hunting dogs being particularly susceptible.

This particular species is only about $\frac{1}{2}''$ to $\frac{3}{4}''$ long, and it lives in the intestines. The animals are generally dull, starey-eyed, thin and anaemic; the coat very poor; the breath foul. As the name implies, the parasites hook themselves on to the lining of the intestines and suck the blood, causing anaemia, and they can quickly weaken the cat if allowed to progress without treatment.

In hunting districts, where hookworms of this species may be present, there may be regular re-infestation, particularly in the summer months. The eggs and larvae may be eaten and the larvae can also enter the body by burrowing through the skin. The eggs, which are excreted by the animal, are so small that diagnosis is only possible by microscope examination.

Sherley's Worming Cream quickly clears infestations of Hookworm Uncinaria. The many other species of Hookworm, particularly in hot countries, require special drugs which need to be administered under veterinary supervision.

TAPEWORMS

If your cat is suffering from Tapeworms, you will nearly always notice segments in the motions. These will be small, seed-like objects, white or greyish-white in colour, which can sometimes be seen to contract and expand.

It is usually tapeworms which affect adult cats, although Roundworms may appear at the same time. Owing to the number of sources it is practically impossible to prevent worm infestation however well the cat is looked after. Tapeworms are exceedingly prolific in egg production, and the excreta of a worm-infested cat is frequently teeming with segments which contain thousands of eggs. These may be carried a long way from where they were originally deposited and worm eggs which have become dried by wind and sun are carried far and wide in dust—hence the importance of burning the droppings, particularly after worming.

If tapeworms are not expelled they sometimes leave the bowel and move up into the stomach; here they can set up irritation followed by vomiting. In such a case worms are sometimes brought up and may block the entrance to the windpipe or even set up asphyxia.

All tapeworms have an intermediary host—in cats the most common host, the flea, eats the eggs as they are passed from the cat. These eggs develop inside the flea into the embryo head, and when the cat eats the flea, tapeworms result. Other sources of infection are rodents and farm animals. If a cat is kept clear from fleas he is unlikely to get the common kinds of tapeworm—so take appropriate measures to deal with fleas, when eliminating tapeworms.

The symptoms of tapeworms are—bad breath; variable or depraved appetite; staring coat; occasional vomitting; diarrhoea or constipation or these two alternately. Segments of the worms may be found in the region of the anus and in the excreta. Eczema is also often induced and cannot be cured so long as worms remain. Adult cats may, however, be infested with tapeworms without showing any marked or noticeable symptoms, therefore if in doubt dose them twice each year.

Tapeworms in their intermediate forms are transmissible to humans and although not easily conveyed, they do at times cause serious illness, so that it is important also for the sake of one's family, to keep cats free from worms.

Recent scientific research has resulted in the development of Sherley's Tapeworm Tablets, a simple safe, amazingly effective remedy which brings quick relief from all tapeworms in adult cats of six months and over. Large scale trials and universal use for some years have proved the efficacy of this new remedy. **Prior fasting or purging are not necessary,** although it is helpful to give a dose of Lik-a-Med Cream Laxative the evening before to ensure maximum effect.

A single dose of Sherley's Tapeworm Tablets is sufficient, in all but rare cases, to turn all the tapeworms in the animal into a white lifeless mass within the intestines, which quickly disintergrates and is expelled with the excrement. Normally there is no need for the frequent treatment necessary with ordinary worm capsules. It should be realised, however, that animals can become re-infested, and only in such cases is further dosing necessary, but this in no way reflects on the efficacy of the treatment. The absence of tapeworm segments from the excrement will be evidence in itself that the initial treatment is successful and it is usually completely effective within about 8—10 hours.

The effect of giving Sherley's Tapeworm Tablets is wholly beneficial and although on rare occasions there may be slight temporary diarrhoea, discomfort, or even vomiting, this will not affect the beneficial action of the treatment. No after-treatment is called for and provided the tablets are not brought up whole, enough should have been absorbed to prove effective. So striking are the above advantages that Sherley's Tapeworm Tablets represent a revolution in the treatment of one of the most serious menaces to the health and well-being of both cats and dogs.

CHINCHILLA-BLUE PERSIAN CROSS KITTEN

CHAPTER VI
The Treatment of Illness

INTRODUCTORY NOTES

When the first issue of the Sherley's Cat Book was published over fifty years ago, the cat was not at all well catered for by veterinary surgeons, who were mainly occupied dealing with animals of the farm, and the horse. Nowadays, however, veterinary surgeons with special skill in the treatment of pets are available in all parts of the country.

Also, scientific research and general hygiene have progressed by leaps and bounds so that many of the diseases in pets are now preventable or curable. Nevertheless, there are still many conditions, some beyond the understanding of man, where diligent and intelligent nursing of the sick are of vital importance.

Nor is it necessary nowadays to deprive your pet of the best skill available on the ground of expense. All over the U.K. the R.S.P.C.A., or other animal welfare societies maintain clinics that provide free treatment for those unable to afford private veterinary service. These clinics ensure that no animal shall fail to have access to the highest skill when suffering and **when your cat is unwell the proper person to diagnose and treat the patient is a veterinary surgeon.**

But the Sherley's Cat Book goes all over the world and is relied upon by many in remote places for help and guidance when no veterinary surgeon is within reach. With such people in mind we have endeavoured to make this book as full and as understandable as possible, so that suffering may be reduced in these particular circumstances. Moreover, it has proved of help to many who have been able to understand what is afoot in cases of illness, and have been able to nurse the patient more efficiently and to prove a greater help to the veterinary surgeon in the arduous task of attending to the daily—and nightly—wants of the patient.

EXAMINATION FOR ILLNESS

Cats are normally exceptionally healthy and active members of the household, gay and friendly, therefore when your pet cat goes off his food and curls up miserably for hours, drooping and huddled, some illness should be suspected and the first thing you should do is to take his temperature. (See page 90).

You will probably know whether he is constipated, or suffering from diarrhoea—whether he has actually passed water or only tried to do so—if there is any vomiting or " retching "—whether the diarrhoea or vomit is bloodstained, etc. If there is any lameness or limping—if the breathing is quick or with difficulty—if he is very thirsty. These are important to know before proceeding to examine the patient.

Cats can be somewhat difficult to handle when they are ill and should be handled very gently indeed . . . so begin by watching and listening.

Do you see any discharge from the **eyes**, and if so, is it watery or thick and what colour is it? Is the opening of each pupil the same size? Cats have a third eyelid known as " the haw " and if this can be seen in the corner of the eye it may be a sign of oncoming illness or poor condition, such as is commonly due to a fur ball in the stomach. Examine the **nose** too, it is usually moist and cool; is it very hot and dry—is there any discharge? Do not rely only upon the feel of the nose—even in fevers it is not always dry.

Examine the **ears**; is he scratching them—is there a lot of wax or a discharge of pus inside the ear cavity? Notice if there is any dribbling from the mouth. If there are **choking sounds** and the cat claws at its mouth, then the teeth, tongue or throat may be involved—perhaps a bone may be stuck somewhere inside the mouth or down the throat. **Move his head** up and down and sideways. (See Sharp Bones, Needles, etc., page 121). **Open the mouth wide** to see if there is any inflammation or if there is a bone in the throat. **Pass the hand under the jaw** and around the neck for swellings, the result of an abscess. Note whether the **breath** is offensive, also examine the colour and condition of the **tongue** and see if the **teeth** are covered with fur, which unlike tartar, can be wiped off with a piece of wool. The **gums** and the back of the **throat** must be examined at the same time for any growth that may be forming.

Examination of the Body. Gentleness is essential . . . run the hands gently over all the body trying to locate the site of the trouble, watching for any area of special tenderness or unexpected lumps which may indicate an abscess following on after a bite— or in older cats may indicate a growth.

Watch the animal as it walks. Can it jump on to its usual chair? Move the limbs forward and backward and observe whether they are normal and whether this causes pain.

In further examination of the body watch its breathing by observing the flanks; if gentle pressure on the chest causes pain, then one may suspect some inflammation of the lung (broncho-pneumonia), or of the chest wall (pleurisy).

Examination of the Abdomen . . . may be carried out by very gently feeling the contents of the abdomen just in front of the hind legs between fingers and thumb for any general tenderness or any unusual lumps or tender points. For example, a round lump in the rear half of the abdomen which does not yield to pressure might be caused by retention of urine in the bladder or maybe a growth . . . or in most cases, a stone in the bladder. Usually in such cases, one will have noticed the cat trying to pass water without success—or maybe only a dribble—also indicative of the stoppage and needing urgent veterinary attention. Poisoning can follow kidney and bladder inflammation because retention of urine due to the blockage will lead to waste products being retained in the bloodstream instead of being removed by the kidneys and passed to the bladder. (See page 114).

A large lump well forward in the abdomen, just behind the last ribs, might be a HAIR-BALL.

In feeling over the body, particularly of playful kittens, one may even feel the point of a needle coming out through the skin. **It is not uncommon for kittens to pick up a needle** and get it into their mouths or somewhere in the region of the mouth or even down in the stomach where it may eventually exit through the skin.

In female cats, pass the hands along the milk glands to see if there are any swellings due to abscesses or tumours.

The object of this systematic examination is to ascertain, if possible, the nature and the site of the ailment. Where the illness is obscure and is obviously severe, it will need expert veterinary attention with perhaps a surgical operation, or medical treatment over a period. The symptoms noted should be mentioned to the veterinary surgeon.

TEMPERATURE AND THERMOMETER

The normal temperature of a cat should be taken in the rectum and is approximately 101.5°F. (38.6°C.) but may vary a fraction up or down . . . the lazy neuter cat slightly lower whereas an active young cat or kitten may register up to 102°F. (38.9°C.). A temperature reading above 102°F. (38.9°C.) would indicate a fever.

Example of Temperature Chart for Several Cats
Normal=101.5°F.=38.6°C.)

Date	BOBBY			SUZY			PATCH			TOMMY		
	9 a.m.	2 p.m.	7 p.m.	9 a.m.	2 p.m.	7 p.m.	9 a.m.	2 p.m.	7 p.m.	9 a.m.	2 p.m.	7 p.m.
Nov. 1	102.4	103	104	101	101.5	102	103	102.5	102	101.2	101.7	101.5
2	101.4	102	103.4									
3	103	102.4	102									
4												
5				The figures above are Fahrenheit.								
6				Centigrade equivalents—								
7	101=38.3	101.5=38.6	102=38.9	103=39.4	104=40							

Taking the temperature of a cat requires two persons . . . one to hold the cat and the other " operating ", and it should only be taken when serious illness or fever is suspected, or when necessary as a guide to how a patient is progressing.

The usual human clinical thermometer is best for cats and kittens, preferably a thick ½ minute type. Care should be taken not to let the movements of the cat in a sideways direction snap off the mercury end in the rectum. With the modern ½ minute thermometer bearing the official N.P.L. stamp this is fortunately a rare occurrence.

The temperature should always be taken in the rectum (inside, immediately under the tail), because this is the only place where one can get a correct registration. The temperature taken in the groin or under the forearm is unreliable. With patience and quiet, cats do not usually object to the correct rectal method. First see that the thermometer is clean and has been shaken down well below 98°F. The mercury (blob-end) should be well vaselined and about 1 inch inserted into the rectum and held there **for a full minute.** Always wash and rinse the thermometer under the tap after use so that it is hygienically clean, then shake it down to well below 98° again, ready for future use. In the sickroom, in between use, the thermometer can be kept in very weak Antiseptic Lotion in a small jar or similar container.

While a cool damp nose is associated with health, it is not always dry in illness, even in fevers, so do not rely on the nose as an indication of temperature.

PULSE

The character and frequency of the pulse may be ascertained by placing the fingers over the femoral artery—which is found on the inside of the thigh—where it crosses the thigh bone. The number of the beats per minute in health varies according to the size of the cat, from about 90 for kittens to about 70 for large cats. The accurate meaning and assessment of the pulse in cats is, however, so unreliable in respect of what it implies, that it is not recommended that anything other than the rate per minute will be recorded. Even the lifting of a cat onto a table for examination will double the rate of the pulse for the time being, so it will be readily seen that alarming conclusions can be drawn unless one has had special experience.

ADMINISTERING MEDICINES

It would obviously be a more simple operation to give medicines, etc., if they could all be pleasant-tasting or tasteless and all tablets sugar-coated but this is not always possible and even these may be rejected. These notes therefore include advice on administration in any circumstances which may arise.

Before giving any unpleasant or repeated dose of medicine to a cat be sure he does not see you opening or mixing the medicine as he will quickly recognise the preliminaries and what is to follow. When giving liquid medicine, unless he is a very quiet type he may be very difficult and it is advisable to put him in a bag with just his head outside or in a " duffle " bag with a draw-string, or to wrap him in a good thick rug to prevent being scratched. Always wear gloves if you are not sure of the temper of the animal, at least until the cat is secure or if you are not expert in handling cats, because they are always inclined to be nervous and even vicious in these circumstances, particularly with strangers.

Whenever possible, medicine should be given either in powder or tablet form made pleasant with syrup, or in fudge, or in the form of a small sugar coated pill. Any fairly tasteless medicine could be mixed with a little of a favourite food or a sardine or with a little milk.

Otherwise in all cases it is necessary to open the mouth and this is best done by placing the left hand over the cat's head and with the thumb and first finger gently press the cheek on each side when, as a rule, the mouth is opened. If the cat is obstinate and refuses to open the mouth just separate the teeth with the nails of the first fingers and thumb of the right hand, continuing to squeeze the cheeks so that when the mouth is open it can be kept so, and at the same time raise the nose. **If giving powders,** when the mouth is open shake the dry powder on the back of the tongue and, this done, close the mouth quickly and keep the mouth and nose closed for a few seconds until the powder has been swallowed.

A tablet or pill is given in the same way; the mouth must be well opened, the nose well raised, the **pill** then dropped right at the back of the mouth, and, as in the case of giving a powder, the mouth must be quickly closed and kept closed for a few minutes —at the same time stroking the front of the throat to encourage the cat to swallow. When giving **capsules** these should only be very small ones. Special forceps designed to hold a pill while it is pushed over the root of the tongue, save many a nasty bite or graze to the hands. Some cats will " pocket " tablets in the side of the mouth for several minutes and then reject them again and again and it does sometimes help if a tasty morsel of food is offered by a second person whilst the cat's mouth is held closed. Usually the act of swallowing is signalled by the cat's tongue licking the front of his mouth.

If a laxative is necessary, then Sherley's Lik-a-Med is recommended. It is in the form of a palatable cream and just dabbed on his nose or mouth, he will lick it off without any difficulty . . . and the Lik-a-Med acts gently and without griping.

When **liquid medicine** is necessary, then a medicine or feeding spoon with curved spout something after the style of a teapot spout, or a fountain pen filler are the most suitable for giving either liquid medicine or food. The cat's head should be firmly held with the left hand so as to prevent the cat opening the mouth wide, at the same time raising the nose; the spout of the spoon should then be placed between the side cheek and teeth and the liquid **slowly** poured into the mouth, when it will trickle between the teeth on to the tongue and the cat will swallow it. A cat hates to have a hard metal spoon of medicine forced between its teeth and keeps biting on it and otherwise making a fuss so that half the medicine is lost by going over the head as well as on to the person giving it. Some cats are more readily dosed with a plastic spoon. With tiny kittens a fountain pen filler can be used as a feeder by piercing the teat end. (See page 43).

In giving liquid medicine of any kind it should always be given very slowly, a little at a time, and care should be taken not to raise the head so far as to allow it to enter the larynx, as this would cause the cat to choke. With a very difficult cat which refuses the medicine and foams at the mouth it is possible to hold the mouth uppermost by grasping the " scruff " of the neck and pulling the head back. Then gently and slowly drop the liquid on the upper lip when he will start lapping with his tongue.

With oily liquids a little dropped on his nostril or even on his fore-limb will cause him to lick it off when you let him go.

Every possible precaution, as mentioned above, should be taken to avoid being scratched by the cat and if you should suffer any scratches or bites you should immediately wash thoroughly and treat the wounds freely with Amplexol or Antiseptic Lotion.

Dosage of Medicine and Size of Patient. The effective dose of a medicine does not increase proportionately with the size and weight of the animal. For example, because a cat weighing 8 lbs. needs 1 teaspoon of medicine (an eighth of an ounce) it does not follow that a human being about 10 stone (140 lbs.) needs eighteen times the dose of the cat, i.e., more than two ounces! So whatever the remedy, always read the instructions on the label first and know what you are doing and follow the doses given on the box or bottle of medicine.

Some drugs have a unique effect on certain species of animals. A classic example is strychnine, which is often poisonous to cats in doses that would not harm a human baby. Some human constipation remedies contain strychnine, so avoid giving human laxatives to a cat. Morphia in the case of a dog, is so safe that it may take two or three grains to obtain the same effect on a dog that a quarter grain dose has on a human adult, whereas if used on a cat it is more likely to cause excitement and even hysteria rather than having a calming effect. Castor Oil should not be given to cats—to some it acts almost like a poison.

ENEMAS

It is occasionally necessary in cases of obstruction of the bowels to give an enema. This is best done with the smallest size Enema Syringe. **In giving an enema care must be taken to exclude all air by holding the tube point uppermost and pressing the bulb gently until the liquid appears at the aperture and the tube is then slowly and gently inserted into the rectum as far as possible.** Always give enemas slowly, a little at a time, to avoid causing too much internal pressure and after giving, keep the hind quarters slightly raised for a few minutes, holding the root of the tail down closely to the body. In constipation this will give the fluid an opportunity of soaking into the hard masses, which cannot usually be passed until they have become softened. As the flow is by gravity, the lower the container or funnel is held, the slower the flow.

For Constipation the best enema to give is one teaspoonful of Glycerin mixed with two small tablespoons of tepid water or 1 tablespoonful to a pint. Soapy water may be used if Glycerin is not available. Well lubricate the stem of the syringe with lard or Vaseline and introduce it into the bowl for about one inch.

A second quantity may be given if the first does not operate successfully in a few minutes. (See also Constipation).

Enemas are also used as a method of administering food when it is necessary to rest the stomach, when the patient is too weak to take nourishment through the mouth—for instance when a queen is exhausted through protracted kittening troubles, or where there is gastric trouble with continuous vomiting. Nourishment to be given in the form of an enema is given very slowly with the container only slightly higher than the patient and must of course be in liquid form, Lactol mixed as directed, being best. Give from a teaspoonful to a tablespoonful, and in cases of great exhaustion add from five drops to half a teaspoonful of brandy according to size of patient.

HYPODERMIC SYRINGES

The coming of the antibiotic drugs, such as penicillin and the bacteriostatic drugs, of which the sulpha drugs are the outstanding example, together with the injections of vaccines and sera now so effective in the prevention and treatment of the distemper group of diseases, has meant that a great deal of medicine is no longer given by the mouth but by injection under the skin, through the skin into the substance of muscle (intramuscular), into a body cavity such as the chest (intra-thoracic) or abdomen (intra-abdominal), or into a vein (intravenous).

The hypodermic syringe, its use, sterilization and storage are necessary knowledge to the feline nurse. Probably only one size will be necessary, two cubic centimetres capacity, i.e. 2 cc. or ml.

Since in the home and in catteries, the use of syringes is intermittent, they are best purchased in a leak-proof container wherein they can lie for long periods without deterioration, immersed in surgical spirit. When needed all that has to be done is to take the needle and push it firmly on to the tapering nozzle of the syringe and draw several syringefuls of recently boiled water through the instruments to remove all traces of the spirit, as spirit, even in droplets, can adversely affect some injections. Then the needle is introduced into the glass ampoule containing the dose of drug and by pulling on the piston the syringe is filled with the appointed dose. The graduations on the barrel of the syringe ensure the correct amount being available.

If a little air is introduced, hold the syringe point uppermost and press gently on the plunger until a tiny bead of fluid at the tip of the needle indicates that all the air has been expelled. **Air must never accompany the dose into the patient's body,** as it may be germ laden, and if the dose goes into a vein it can endanger life through the formation of an airlock in a bloodvessel.

Some drugs are in a rubber-capped bottle containing a number of doses. In this case the rubber cap is first wiped with a small wad of cotton wool soaked in surgical spirit. If the dose to be removed is, say 2 cc. then the plunger of the syringe is withdrawn so as to contain 2 cc. of air. When the needle is plunged through the rubber cap this 2 cc. of air is driven into the bottle, which should be held inverted (upside down). Then the 2 cc. of the contents is drawn into the syringe. The reason for putting in the same volume of air is to equalise the pressure on either side of the cork. Otherwise, after withdrawal of several doses the thin rubber cap would be sucked into the bottle vacuum and the contents spoiled.

After use, the syringe is dismantled and washed clean, then boiled for five minutes in water, allowed to cool, and then returned to its spirit container ready for the next occasion.

To give a hypodermic injection is not difficult, and an abscess developing as a result of introducing germs under the skin is most unlikely provided the small fold of skin into which the needle penetrates is well swabbed with surgical spirit and provided the syringe and the operator's hands are clean.

Since not a few injections provoke a drug reaction in the form of a swelling at the site, it is far less painful to the cat afterwards if the site has no bone, such as ribs, directly beneath. The lumbar region, a couple of inches right or left of the spine, or a similar site behind the ears, are the best places.

The assistant must now hold the cat to prevent it from struggling or biting and for cats the best way is for the assistant, seated, to hold the cat in a blanket under his arm. Pinch up, between the forefinger and thumb of the left hand, a small fold of skin at the spot where the surgical spirit was dabbed and push the needle firmly for about half an inch into the skin at the top of the fold, the direction of the needle to be such as to keep it close under the skin, but not so close as to risk pricking the skin again. Inject the contents of the syringe by steady pressure on the plunger and then pull the syringe away.

If it has been done neatly and quickly, nine cats out of ten will make little or no sign of having felt anything at all. The smaller the diameter of the needle the more likely is the cat to be unaware of the injection, but the finer the needle bore the slower is the speed of injection. Only experience and personal technique will arrive at the best compromise. Somewhere around 25 to 30 thousandths of an inch (0.025″–0.030″) is a useful size for doses up to 2 cc.

To clean after use, draw up water just off the boil into the syringe, squirt it out, and repeat this a few times before dismantling the syringe to put it away.

A wire should be kept in the needle when not in use and several needles are supplied with the hypodermic syringes which are specially made for use with small animals.

NURSING

Good and careful nursing is very important in some cases, particularly in distemper or contagious feline gastro-enteritis and gastritis. The patient should be left alone as much as possible but in long cases it is necessary to give nourishment, as generally a very sick cat refuses to take any food voluntarily, and in consequence would eventually die from exhaustion. Therefore, give what is necessary and then leave the animal quiet and alone until it is time to feed again.

If the patient will take it, Lactol or Lactol in water should generally be left with the patient. A few laps will often be found to induce it to take some food voluntarily; in some cases, however, water does harm, as in gastritis, and then a lump of ice in a perforated dish like a soap dish can be substituted and placed handy for the cat to get at. Glucose water, say a teaspoon of glucose dissolved in a half pint of water, will keep a cat alive for a long time, but cats when ill will often refuse even this. Gentle coaxing or some delectable morsel to smell or taste often helps to arouse the appetite. Very often a few drops of the odorous oil from a freshly opened tin of sardines will start hunger pangs, but carnivores of the cat and dog family are adapted for starvation and a few days without food is rarely harmful. Even a Sherley-Vite Tablet or a few crumbs of a tablet mixed with honey or a tasty morsel placed on the lips often helps.

Before beginning to feed a cat forcibly, all kinds of tempting foods—see section " Foods for Invalids "—should be offered, as even the smallest quantity taken voluntarily does more good than artificial feeding, which they dislike more than anything, although it is often absolutely necessary in bad cases if the cat is to be saved.

Cats that are very ill require just as much—or more—care and good nursing at night as during the day, for it is then that the system is lowest and most feeble.

Even if the cat seems willing to take it, during the illness **do not give large quantities of food at a time** as this will induce indigestion, probably with vomiting and diarrhoea as well, which are most weakening. Better, give small quantities at frequent intervals, say every hour or two. Each time liquid food or medicine of a sticky or greasy nature is given the cats' lips should be cleaned with a damp sponge or a piece of medicated wool, and dried.

To give a liquid food use a smooth plastic teaspoon, which is excellent for giving liquids to sick cats as it can be inserted between the teeth and cheek and the fluid slowly poured into the mouth. This obviates the necessity for opening the mouth and also the risk of being bitten, as the mouth can be kept closed and the head slightly pulled back and up with the left hand whilst feeding with the right. It must all be done very carefully and quietly, otherwise the patient is upset and commences to struggle, which is harmful as it increases the weakness. It is just as easy to feed a cat on one side as the other. A right-handed person feeding on the left side should stand in front of the cat, and if on the right side, to the right and rather behind it.

When there is discharge from the eyes and nose, gently clean the eyes frequently and also every time after feeding, using a warm weak solution of Sherley's Eye Lotion, or warm water, applied with a piece of wool. The nose may be cleansed with Sherley's Antiseptic Lotion diluted with warm water.

If a cat is very weak and low, it is wise to keep it warm by placing **a warm (not very hot) water bottle in its basket.** Always test the bottle carefully holding it against your bare arm for some minutes after filling or the patient may be scalded or receive serious or even fatal burns if it is too hot. **Always** wrap the bottle securely in a bag or blanket. The sickroom temperature should be kept steady at say 65°F. (18°C.), though in lung infections (bronchitis, pneumonia, pleurisy) it may be raised to about 70°F. (21°C.).

FOODS FOR INVALIDS

The feeding of sick cats is always a great problem, and because of their fastidious nature they must be treated in a totally different way from all other animals. They should have anything which they will take voluntarily.

When a cat is really ill, food of any kind, including Lactol or milk and even water is frequently refused. If water will be taken, however, the patient should be allowed to have it (except in cases of gastritis—See page 138) as it may improve the appetite. Often where Lactol or milk is refused, water will be accepted, and even should it fail to create an appetite—as animals can live a long time on water alone—it will help to keep the cat alive. Frequently, however, a cat, after taking a few laps will then eat a little food.

When a cat refuses food it should, if possible, be given nourishment from a spoon (see section on " Nursing "), but before this is attempted many different varieties of food should be offered, since food taken voluntarily is of greater value than forcibly administered.

Lactol, mixed as for invalids, is excellent; it may be given alone or with **a raw egg** beaten up in it. From five to ten drops of brandy —according to the size of the cat—may be added.

Juice squeezed from raw meat is good (special presses may be bought for this purpose), and one or two tablespoonfuls may be given alternately with the Lactol, or mixed with it. A beaten up raw egg is sometimes liked. Beef essence, preferably in jelly form, is very nourishing, as is also rabbit jelly made at home, which is preferred by some cats.

Fish, boiled, fried or raw, may tempt them to eat. Where a cat is suffering from an illness affecting the nose and the sense of smell as in contagious feline gastro-enteritis, catarrh, etc.—a coarse fish, such as a fresh bloater, is more likely to be eaten. When food cut up and offered on a plate is refused, if the owner puts the whole fresh bloater on a table in the room and goes away leaving it there, the cat will sometimes jump up and eat it—**cats love to steal their food.**

Sardines may also meet with approval.

A few drops of Gin (perhaps 15 to 20 drops for a large cat) placed on the cat's tongue, often acts as an appetizer. Administer the gin before offering the food, then go out of the room and you may find when you get back after a while that the meat you have been so anxiously waiting for the cat to take, has disappeared.

Different kinds of meat may be tried (raw or cooked) rabbit and poultry; also liver (grilled because it has more flavour then) especially grilled chicken livers, of which cats are very fond; grilled kidney, a sheep's kidney, sheep's milt, or sheep's brains boiled. Cats usually prefer beef to mutton, but invariably like horse flesh best. They will sometimes gnaw at a large slice of meat after refusing some which has been cut up.

If possible, offer a whole small bird, such as a sparrow, feathers and all, immediately after it has been killed and whilst it is still warm. A cat will often take this when all else has been refused, and a freshly killed mouse may also be very tempting.

If nothing tempts the cat to eat voluntarily then Lactol or selected jellies and liquid foods from those advised above must be given out of a spoon. In giving jelly use an egg-spoon which has first been dipped in hot water so that the jelly will not stick to it. Pick up a small quantity in the spoon, raise the cat's nose, open its mouth, and slip the jelly into the back of the mouth, when it will usually be swallowed unless the throat is very sore.

For a change, give strong meat-tea made with two ounces each of lean mutton, beef and veal, which should be cut small and very lightly stewed for two or three hours in half a pint of water and then strained off through butter-cloth.

When a cat is fairly quiet it can be fed with half-inch cubes of raw meat given off the point of a wooden skewer. The mouth should be opened wide and the meat quickly placed in the back of the throat; the mouth should then be held closed until the meat has been swallowed. Half a dozen pieces may be given at a time in this way.

Sherley-Vite Tablets are an excellent tonic food for cats in a weak condition—they help them to digest and assimilate the food that is being given. Also Lintox, added to Lactol or water helps to rebuild the strength.

DISINFECTING AND DEFESTING AFTER INFECTION

Apart from the normal necessary hygiene precautions, the main objects are to prevent spread of the disease, fever, epidemic or other condition and also to prevent subsequent re-infection by the virus or germs etc., or re-infestation by the parasites etc.

There are three aspects of disinfection . . .

1. Personal washing of oneself and of clothing etc., worn during contact with the infection.

2. Utensils, bedding, collars, etc., used or worn by the patient(s).

3. The actual sick-room or furniture or any parts of the building.

The measures taken in cases of the minute viruses which are responsible for most epidemic diseases in human and animals are very different from those measures necessary following outbreaks of skin diseases due to fleas, lice, mange parasites or ringworm.

Personal hygiene of self and of clothing in epidemics means frequent washing and scrubbing with soap or detergent and water, followed by rinsing with fresh water to which has been added a good safe disinfectant such as Amplexol or Sherley's Antiseptic Lotion or Kennel Fluid. After any contact with infectious disease it is important to change outer clothing (overall, cap, etc.) and to wash hands as above. Shoes should be disinfected by wiping the feet before entering and when leaving—on a mat or a sack kept at the door, soaked or sprinkled daily with the diluted disinfectant.

Overalls, caps, etc., need to be separately washed (and boiled if possible) and rinsed in the disinfectant.

Utensils, bowls, dishes, spoons, etc., after first cleaning off dirt and food particles . . . place them in water which is already boiling and keep it on the boil for 10 to 15 minutes—or sterilise under steam for ten minutes.

Cage timbers and metal parts can be sterilised by lightly applying a blowlamp, taking care on plated and soldered parts.

Care must be taken in choosing the disinfectant used on cats because they cannot tolerate phenols and strong bleaches, therefore use only disinfectants which are guaranteed as safe for pets and use them in accordance with the directions printed on the label.

Where infectious disease has occurred in a house, the carpets, etc., where the patient has been should be sprayed with a weak solution of Formalin—a teaspoonful to three pints of water—using a fine spray or syringe for the purpose. (Special care is necessary in handling the concentrated Formalin—which you can buy from your chemist—and he will advise you regarding the handling and mixing.) This spraying should be repeated daily for two or three days, and anything movable to which it is possible to give such treatment should be boiled or else baked in an oven that is just not hot enough to burn. Where it is possible to do so the rooms of the house should be disinfected in the same manner as recommended for catteries below.

Fumigation of rooms in dwelling houses or Catteries after infectious virus diseases . . . first of all the floors need a good scrub then fumigation with a sulphur or formalin candle to fill the room with disinfectant vapour. Where possible all surfaces of walls as well as floors should be damp for the gases will then dissolve in the moisture and attack the viruses or germs more effectively. Fumigation candles must be used in accordance with the makers' directions and according to size of room etc., usually stated on the pack.

Where parasites (from fleas to tiny mange parasites) are concerned, first make sure that any cats, or other animals to be introduced into the premises have not been infected at all and are not therefore carriers of latent infection from the recent outbreak—and this may entail veterinary examination—most efficient of all is to fumigate with one or more gammexane candles burned in the same manner as for fumigation above, and according to the maker's directions on the pack.

With all gas-producing candles, the directions specify one candle for so many cubic feet of space, so it will be necessary to check the room dimensions to ensure that the gas will be at full strength and all cracks around windows, door frames, etc., will need to be tightly stopped up with wedges of folded newspaper or sealed thoroughly with some kind of adhesive tape.

Place the candle in a basin or large tin in the centre of the room, light it and retreat, shutting the door quickly, lock it and remove the key so that no-one enters inadvertently. Do not enter or open windows sooner than the directions advise, usually after 1 hour or more, then thorough ventilation to completely disperse the fumes is absolutely essential before cats are brought into the room or building.

If the gas candles are not obtainable, after scrubbing leave to dry, then sprinkle Vamoose Pet Powder (available in puffers and 8 oz. sprinklers) over all surfaces and brush any surplus into crevices and cracks, where the future pets cannot lick the powder, either directly or from contact with their fur. Carpets can be treated similarly, including any underfelts, etc.

Your local Veterinary Surgeon or Official of your local Animal Welfare Society will be pleased to advise regarding the disinfection in order to ensure that there is no likelihood of recurrence of the trouble when healthy cats are brought into the house or Cattery.

In cases of Infectious Feline Enteritis particularly, it is recommended that new cats should **not** be introduced into the same premises within four to six months.

PAINLESS DEATH (Euthanasia)

Sometimes despite devoted care, the patient reaches the stage in its illness when it is essential to end its suffering. Veterinary Surgeons usually inject one of the sleep-producing drugs known as Pentobarbitone (or Nembutal) into a vein in a sufficient dose to ensure death. This is by far the most humane way of ending a cat's life.

In Britain the drug is subject to our Poison Laws but may be obtainable outside Britain and it can also be given by mouth, which is a great advantage, 2–5 grains placed on the tongue and a dose for this purpose may be obtained from a veterinary surgeon by an owner. In places far from towns in foreign parts, the local doctors can assist in supplying the required barbiturate for injection, or by mouth. Pentobarbitone (Nembutal), can be given by mouth. Two of the $1\frac{1}{2}$ grain capsules can have their contents poured into a dry spoon and then placed on the cat's tongue. Sleep is usually induced in 5 to 10 minutes.

This dose will ensure a deep sleep, when the animal can be either dealt with by a Vet., when unconscious, without it being aware of anything being done, or it can be conveyed to his surgery in this state for the final dose. There is no more painless way of ending the suffering of one's pet.

While in this state, one of various methods may be employed to make sure that death is complete and painless. An overdose of the same drug, chloroform lethal chamber, or a cat pistol, are all perfectly humane and may be used with the aid of the drug previously given.

If it is necessary to destroy a cat which is fierce and you cannot get hold of him by the back of the neck, it is best to use a cat grasper, a form of lasso, consisting of stiffish cord. About 6–7 feet of this is passed through a 4–5 foot length of conduit or gas tubing and is securely lashed at its far end from the operator so that a loop can be formed to be passed round the cat's neck. As soon as this is accomplished, the cord is pulled tight to secure the cat and held at the end nearest the operator.

In Great Britain, it is usual, of course, to entrust painless destruction either to a Veterinary Surgeon or to one of the clinics of the R.S.P.C.A., or P.D.S.A. where they have trained and expert staff in this branch of their work and moreover one can be sure that they use the latest approved methods.

It is cruel to give poisons such as Prussic Acid or Strychnine so often used many years ago, apart from the dangers to the operators which are very real with these two poisons. Under no conditions should Strychnine be permitted as a means of destruction as it causes very great suffering by holding all the muscles of the body in a state of severe cramp and although the animal cannot cry out it is in very great pain for some time before death eventually brings relief.

In an emergency when an animal is in agony as the result of an accident, and suitable help cannot be obtained, one may have to use a shot gun. The muzzle should be held about one or two feet away from the animal's head and the aim should be in the region of 45° behind the head from the axis of the body so that the bullets enter behind the ear and into the brain. Make sure that after they have passed through the head the pellets will be embedded in soft ground and will not ricochet in such a way as to injure bystanders. It is always a safe rule that anyone present should be made to stand behind the one who is actually firing the gun.

The average life span of a cat is about 12 years, but many have been known to live to 15 to 20 years, but if your cat is ailing and very weak, after the age of 10, 11 or 12 years there is very little hope of him recovering to health and more happy years, so it is often kinder to have him put to sleep rather than suffer in his old age. Therefore, if your cat is very elderly and in obvious incurable pain, your veterinary surgeon can put him to sleep very gently and quickly without further suffering. You will miss him but can console yourself with the knowledge that he will be at peace.

SOME USEFUL WEIGHTS AND MEASURES

60 drops or minims........1 dram	2 dessertspoonfuls...1 tablespoonful
8 drams.................1 ounce	1½ to 2 tablespoonfuls..1 fluid ounce
20 fluid ounces............1 pint	(according to size)
20 grains...............1 scruple	1 litre...................1.8 pints
3 scruples................1 dram	1 gallon.................4½ litres
1 dram.............1 teaspoonful	3 pennies.................1 ounce
4 teaspoonfuls.....1 tablespoonful	Half-a-crown.............½ ounce

SKELETON OF THE CAT

(and ordinary descriptions of the bones)

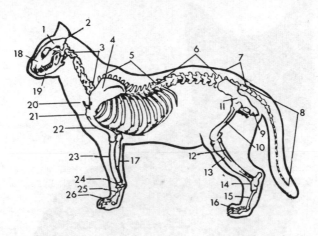

(1) CRANIUM (Top of Skull)

(2) OCCIPUT (Back ,,　,,)

(3) CERVICAL VERTEBRAE (Neck)

(4) SCAPULA (Shoulder Blade)

(5) DORSAL VERTEBRAE
(Top Back)

(6) LUMBAR VERTEBRAE (Back)

(7) SACRUM VERTEBRAE
(Hindquarters)

(8) COCCYGEAL VERTEBRAE (Tail)

(9) PUBIS (Lower Pelvis)

(10) FEMUR (Thigh)

(11) PELVIS (Hindquarters)

(12) FIBULA (Thinner Rear Leg
Bone)

(13) TIBIA (Thicker Rear Leg
Bone)

(14) TARSUS (Rear Ankle)

(15) METATARSUS (Rear Foot)

(16) REAR PHALANGES (Toes)

(17) ULNA (Rear " Forearm "
Bone)

(18) NASAL BONE

(19) MANDIBLE (Lower Jaw)

(20) STERNUM (Breast Bone)

(21) RIBS

(22) HUMERUS (Upper Arm—
Foreleg)

(23) RADIUS (Front " Forearm "
Bone)

(24) CARPUS (" Wrist "—Front
Ankle)

(25) METACARPUS (" Hand "—
Front Foot)

(26) FRONT PHALANGES (Toes)

SHORT-HAIRED TABBY

106

CHAPTER VII
Diseases, Ailments & Accidents

(Arranged alphabetically for convenience of reference.)
For full list of medicines, etc., see page 161.

The medicines prescribed in these pages may be given with confidence, having been used for many years with the greatest success. Sherley Products are prepared under strict hygienic conditions from the purest drugs, in accordance with modern veterinary practice.

Sherley's internal remedies are often of the tablet type, the advantages of medicines in this form being that they take up less room, travel better, and keep good for an indefinite time if kept in a cool, dry place and not exposed to light. Also tablets may be administered crushed and mixed in with solid food or milk.

In all towns in the United Kingdom and in many overseas countries, Chemists, Pet Stores and Corn Merchants stock Sherley's preparations or will obtain them to order. In case of difficulty Sherley's will forward the items required by return of post on receipt of a letter enclosing postal order for the necessary amount plus postage.

A study of these pages will enable the reader to treat correctly many feline illnesses, but where serious illness is suspected then diagnosis and correct treatment are urgent and important, and a veterinary surgeon should be consulted as soon as possible.

ABSCESSES

An abscess is a painful swelling containing pus (commonly called matter) and is usually accompanied by a rise in temperature. Unlike a tumour, an abscess generally forms very quickly and becomes a painful and inflamed swelling. Besides being the result of a punctured wound (usually a cat bite which has been allowed to heal up too quickly) it is not uncommon for an abscess to form in the cat's throat just behind the angle of the jaw as a result of a fish bone lodging there or from the cat playing with a needle and cotton and getting the needle in the throat and puncturing the membrane of the gullet.

First it will be necessary to clip the hair as short as possible on and around the inflamed area. When conveniently situated for the application of a bandage (if your cat will permit bandaging), apply warm poultices on lint, the poultices not warmer than you can bear on the back of your hand, and cover with a piece of plastic film overlapping all round to keep in the heat. Cover this again with a pad of cotton wool and then bandage comfortably, not tightly. The poultice should be changed every 12 hours.

If your cat will not allow bandaging, then apply not-too-hot cotton wool pads well squeezed out, the oftener the better, for periods of about 10 minutes at a time. Don't make the cat too wet, it is the heat which is required.

When the abscess has come to a head and is soft—and not before—then it needs to be opened freely with a sterilised scalpel (sharp pointed knife) to allow the matter or pus to escape. It is wise to have a veterinary surgeon carry out the actual lancing of the abscess. The wound should then be cleaned with warm dressings of Sherley's Antiseptic Lotion diluted with boiled water and a small piece of lint smeared over liberally with Sherley's Veterinary Ointment, warmed, applied directly to the wound and bandaged to keep it there for about 12 hours. Repeat this dressing twice a day to avoid too rapid healing otherwise the abscess may form again. If the cat will not permit bandaging, then carry out the warm bathing and application of the ointment until healing is complete; meantime keeping the cat warm to avoid a chill.

Abscesses sometimes form in the **gland at the side of the neck,** just behind the jaw and under the ear, giving the cat the appearance of suffering from mumps, but cats do not suffer from mumps and in the absence of veterinary advice the abscess will usually break open by itself although the resulting open wound takes longer to heal. If there should be a fish bone or a needle it can generally be seen and must be extracted. The wound should be kept very clean.

Breast abscesses may occur whilst a queen is suckling her kittens and need special attention. See page 41.

Abscesses are very weakening, and after the illness a course of Lintox Tonic or Energol should be given and these will help to prevent recurrence. The vitamins, etc., in Sherley-Vite Tablets also are beneficial and one tablet should be given each day. Lactol Biscuits should be included in the diet in view of the high degree of nourishment which they contain making them particularly valuable in all cases of weakness and, in general, these additions to the diet will often prevent recurrence.

ACNE (Small Boils)

Acne spots may appear in cats around the nose and chin and may be regarded as minor discharging abscesses and need to be bathed regularly with warm diluted Sherley's Antiseptic Lotion on swabs of cotton-wool. Apply Sherley's Veterinary Ointment for healing, then burn the used swabs and thoroughly scrub the hands with soap and water and rinse in some freshly diluted Antiseptic Lotion.

ANAEMIA

Cats can suffer from anaemia (poorness of blood) when litters are large or when there is some serious internal disease or internal haemorrhage or as a result of severe infestation of lice or other blood-sucking parasites or severe malnutrition. Anaemia in kittens can be due to roundworm infestation. Rickets too, a disease of the bone due to defective absorption of calcium from the bowel, is also accompanied by anaemia, and is more likely in litters which have not had the advantage of fresh air and sunshine.

Anaemia in cats or kittens is indicated by very pale gums and tongue and lack of appetite. If neglected then rickets can develop possibly also due to either or both Vitamin D and Phosphorus deficiency. A daily dose of Cod Liver Oil is needed or Halibut Oil, and minced raw beef, small regular doses of Lintox Tonic and Sherley-Vites (which contain the essential vitamins and phosphates and minerals). Also fresh air, good clean, dry, sleeping quarters and plenty of sunshine are essential.

In severe cases of anaemia where the housing and feeding have been perfect in every way and there are no parasites, then your Veterinary Surgeon should examine the patient for possible internal derangement. See Parasites, also Rickets.

ANAL GLAND INFLAMMATION

This trouble does not occur in cats, whereas in dogs Anal Gland Inflammation is not uncommon.

ANUS—PROLAPSE OF

This sometimes occurs as the result of straining when a cat has some irritation of the lower bowel and, due to constipation or diarrhoea, the lower bowel or rectum may protrude for an inch or more. It requires immediate treatment, as if not relieved it becomes very inflamed and swollen. Veterinary assistance should be obtained as the protruding part will need to be carefully returned and it may be necessary for the veterinary surgeon to put temporary stitches in the anus to retain the prolapsed part or in bad cases to remove the prolapses by operation.

If veterinary assistance is not available then vaseline the protruding part, hold the cat up by the hind legs and apply gentle pressure with the fingers, when it may slip back into place. Avoid all forceful manipulation as the intestines are easily ruptured, with the danger of peritonitis as a sequel.

APOPLEXY

This is extremely rare in cats except when wrongly fed. The blood vessels become weakened and rupture easily under strain. If apoplexy occurs it is usually in older cats and a veterinary surgeon should be called in as soon as possible, but if not available quiet conditions and a light diet are essential. A daily dose of Sherley's Sedative Tablets will help to keep the animal calm.

ARTHRITIS (Inflamed Joint)

This is unusual in cats but can become troublesome in later life where there has been some earlier injury to a joint . . . or it may be due to some infection . . . or of rheumatic origin. Accidents, such as a person stepping on the feet of a kitten, or a cat falling awkwardly, from a great height on to the hard ground, or when being chased by a dog, cannot be excluded.

In Arthritis there is usually pain present and Sherley's Rheumatine Tablets should be given, and a hot-water bottle (well wrapped) placed under the blanket. The warmth of an infra-red lamp will help to relieve the condition. Be sure the cat is never allowed to become constipated by giving a dose of Lik-a-Med Laxative Cream twice a week. (See also Rheumatism and Paralysis).

110

ASCITES. See Dropsy.

ASTHMA

The so-called Asthma of cats generally affects older animals.
Cats do not suffer from true Asthma—it is really chronic
bronchitis or " bronchial-asthma " and sometimes accompanies
kidney or heart diseases. Asthma attacks occur suddenly and are
very distressing to witness, lasting for about 10 minutes to half
an hour and suddenly ceasing. The cat gasps for breath, is
frightened and usually stands still until the attack passes.

Sherley's Creo-Garlic Pills, which are an internal antiseptic,
help to give relief, also the cat should be given honey to lick
when the cough is troublesome. It is best to seek the advice of a
Veterinary Surgeon so that suitable inhalations and medicines
may be given whenever the attacks occur.

Avoid large feeds. Avoid undue quantities of cold water or
exposure to wet or cold particularly when convalescing after
bronchitis or other chest affections. Gentle exercise only and
careful diet which could consist almost entirely of underdone
meat are essential. Give a medium size weekly dose of Lik-a-Med
Laxative to avoid the cat having to strain. See also Bronchitis.

BAD BREATH (Halitosis)

This often occurs in cats, arising from a disordered stomach,
which is most frequently due to hair-ball and may be due to
worms in young cats; in old cats kidney disease is a frequent
cause. It may also result from an accumulation of tartar on the
teeth causing a softening of the gums and eventually pyorrhoea;
from ulcers in the mouth due to a foreign object such as a bone
wedged in the gum or between the back teeth; diseases of the
lungs; or from chronic inflammation of the nasal passage.

**Amplex-Veterinary Deodorant Tablets or, in very severe cases
Amplex-Clinical Tablets,** will quickly clear the odour and small
regular doses will keep it under control. It should, however, be
noted that the odour may be due to some internal disorder and
would assist in the diagnosis of the basic cause which may need
treatment. Severe cases of bad breath should therefore always
have veterinary attention.

If the odour is due to disordered stomach either dose for worms,
if their presence is suspected, or give Lik-a-Med Laxative Cream,
to be followed in each case by a course of Gastrine Tablets.

Lactol Biscuits are strongly recommended as part of the staple diet in cases of stomach disorder. See also Hair-Ball.

For an accumulation of tartar the teeth should be scaled with a Tooth Scraper—an operation best left to veterinary skill, as a sedative will probably be required, also loose teeth are usually present in advanced cases and require removal. Cleaning the teeth and mouth daily with Amplexol will reduce the odour.

Mouth Ulcers should be painted twice daily with a 2 per cent solution of Nitrate of Silver. Diet should be light and very little meat should be given; Lactol, Lactol Biscuits with milk or soup and similar foods are best. There is generally great thirst.

When bad breath is due to lung trouble, inhalation of medicated fumes burned in a small room does good; Sherley's Creo-Garlic Pills should be given for internal antisepsis and the diet must be liberal.

When due to disease in the nasal passages, syringe them once or twice a day with diluted Amplexol and give Creo-Garlic Pills.

In kidney disorder the breath has the characteristic odour of urine, and is accompanied by occasional attacks of vomiting. Kidney disorder is a common cause of bad breath in old animals and veterinary examination of the urine will usually determine this and lead to appropriate treatment. The cat should then be treated for kidney trouble (see page 143).

BALDNESS
(See also Skin Diseases, Eczema and Parasites).

Baldness is always present to a certain extent in cases of skin disease of the irritant type as a result of the scratching, but in such cases the hair grows again as soon as the disease is cured.

Baldness is often associated with the loss of a hormone following unsexing, in which case it is quickly cured by a course of injections of the hormone, administered by the Veterinary Surgeon.

Ordinary baldness sometimes occurs in cats of middle age, but is most often seen in old cats—there is no apparent skin disease, the hair gradually falling out and leaving the skin bare and generally quite clean and shiny, although it may sometimes be hard, dry, and covered with scurf. Other causes may be malnutrition or perhaps in queens suckling very large litters. Baldness is unlikely to occur in cats on which Coatacine is regularly used, as it is an excellent hair tonic.

Treatment.—If the hair follicles have not been destroyed, Coatacine well rubbed into the bare places will stimulate the growth of new hair, and as baldness is in many cases due to weakness, Sherley-Vite Tablets and also Lintox Tonic should be given. Keep the skin clean by regular grooming.

Obstinate cases of baldness are sometimes due to derangement of the thyroid glands—whose function is unbalanced following unsexing. After having eliminated any parasites present and treating the parts regularly with Coatacine for a week or two, if no improvement is noted, then special glandular or other treatment by a Veterinary Surgeon may be necessary.

Where baldness is the **result of very severe burns or scalds** which have destroyed the roots then the hair never grows again.

BILIOUSNESS

The symptoms of this are vomiting. Thirst will be noted in some cases, and is sometimes accompanied by diarrhoea. Food is usually rejected and should not be insisted upon as it is most likely to be vomited. If gastritis and bowel inflammation follow, watch the whites of the eyes for signs of developing jaundice, indicated by their turning yellow. It is most essential that this ailment should not be confused with Nephritis or kidney trouble —the symptoms of which are similar.

Give a dose of Lik-a-Med Laxative Cream last thing at night, and also the following morning, and when this has worked off follow with a course of Sherley's Gastrine Tablets.

BITES (Snakes)

Cats are not usually bitten by snakes because of their careful stalking of any prey they may hunt and their great agility in avoiding dangers such as poisonous snakes. In the event of a snake bite occurring, the cat should receive a dose of snakebite serum with all possible speed and be kept warm and not allowed to move about meanwhile.

BLADDER—DISTENSION OF

Male cats, more especially town-dwelling neuters of lazy habits, may suffer from gravel in the bladder—a collection of sandy deposit which builds up in the bladder, inflaming and blocking the exit and causing an increasing accumulation of urine within the bladder, and the cat is unable to pass water.

The condition is first noticed as the cat is constantly squatting and straining to try to pass urine, sometimes crying out in pain and only a few drops, if any, come away and these may be tinged with blood due to injury to the urethra. The cat becomes restless, uninterested in people or in food and indeed looks worried.

The bladder itself, which is normally within the pelvic cavity, becomes distended into the abdomen and the distended bladder can easily be felt in the back part of the abdomen as a somewhat hard ball about the size of a tangerine, which is painful when pressure is applied. If the condition is not dealt with, poisons accumulate in the bloodstream and the bladder may even rupture. Death is rapid in such event, therefore veterinary attention is extremely urgent.

It is not advisable for an amateur to treat such a case and veterinary assistance should be obtained at once although the blockage of the urinary passage is sometimes impossible to relieve due to the structure of the urethra. If a veterinary surgeon is not available, then destruction of the cat is advisable in order to avoid further suffering.

Over-feeding and lack of exercise, usually in the neutered male cat, are normally the causes, and the diet should be reduced.

If the cat has recovered from the weakening effects of this illness, then the added vitamins, phosphates and minerals in concentrated form which are present in Sherley-Vite Tablets and Lintox Tonic are most beneficial. See also Cystitis.

BLADDER—INFLAMMATION (Cystitis)

Cystitis mainly affects female cats, due to bacterial infection after kittening, or other internal troubles.

The inflammation causes great pain when urine is passed—the cat cries out—the urine is usually cloudy and sometimes with pus or specks of blood. There may be slight increase in the temperature and some indication of constipation. There is fullness of the abdomen and obvious pain when the abdomen is even lightly pressed, although no hard lumps may be present.

Treatment.—Give 3 to 6 grains (approx. 0.2 to 0.4 gram) of Hexamine in a little water twice daily and apply hot fomentations to the abdomen. Give plenty of barley water (if your cat will take it) in preference to plain water and in order to induce the cat to drink frequently add salt to any food given and the diet should be the same as for " Distension " above. Owing to the reluctance of the cat to strain there is a tendency to constipation and a small daily dose of Lik-a-Med Laxative helps.

If there are stones in the bladder an obstruction would lead to uraemic poisoning with fatal results. Urgent veterinary attention is desirable.

If the Cystitis is due to bacterial infection then antibiotic treatment by the veterinary surgeon often relieves the cystitis in a few days.

BLEEDING (Haemorrhage)

External Bleeding from a wound is usually after a fight or an accident and treatment depends upon the seriousness of the injury. The first step is to stop the bleeding as quickly as possible and for this purpose it is important to know whether the bleeding is from a vein or an artery.

Blood from a vein is dark red and oozes out in a steady flow.

Stopping bleeding from a vein is usually possible with a cold water pad, pressed by hand over the part—or if necessary held in position with a firm bandage enclosing the whole part. In a deep wound the artery may be deeply situated therefore note the blood colour and if the wound fills up with blood very quickly then an artery is most likely involved.

Blood from an artery is bright scarlet, spurts out in quick sharp bursts with the heartbeats.

Stopping bleeding from an artery is possible in two ways, according to the position and severity, as follows . . .

· **By finger pressure** on the wound near the end of the artery nearest to the heart. The finger must be perfectly washed with antiseptic or covered with a clean handkerchief. At certain points pressure can be applied to the main arteries where they are over a bone, e.g.

1. The brachial artery about an inch above the elbow joint where pressure will stop the main arterial flow to the front legs below the elbow.

2. The femoral artery, inside the thigh which supplies blood from the heart to the stifle.

3. The Coccygeal artery directly under the base of the tail and which supplies the blood to the whole of the tail.

Using a Tourniquet to stop bleeding. If severe bleeding continues then a tourniquet will be necessary and the procedure is similar to first aid for humans. A large handkerchief folded cornerwise over and over until about 2 in. wide and with the two long corner ends for tying. Enclosed inside the folds in the middle of the handkerchief is a small stone or pad or cork which part is placed over and above the wound—on the side nearest the heart. One half knot is tied in the ends of the handkerchief on the other side of the limb and held whilst a pencil or stick is placed over the knot before the second half of a reef knot is tied. Twisting the stick then tightens the pressure as desired and is then held fast by a separate handkerchief or a bandage around both the limb and the stick.

Never leave a tourniquet tight for more than 10 minutes—slacken off the stick slightly and slowly for 10 seconds every ten minutes, to check whether the bleeding has stopped and to maintain some blood supply to the limb until expert help arrives . . . and obviously . . . in cases of bleeding from a large blood vessel **veterinary help will be urgently necessary.**

If bleeding is from the stomach there is general sickness, and blood is present in the vomited matter and has a dark brown appearance with an objectionable smell. Keep the cat on a diet of Lactol only, mixed as directed for invalids—for a few days. When bleeding is from the lungs the cat coughs somewhat violently and the blood comes from both nostrils. If veterinary help is not available give half a grain of prepared Ergot in a pill every two, three or four hours, according to the size of the cat and the severity of bleeding.

If bleeding is from the bowels, give **adult cats** an enema of a teaspoonful of thick boiled starch to which has been added 5 grains (about a saltspoonful) of powdered Alum, and five drops of Laudanum (if it can be obtained). When bleeding is excessive and the cat is struggling around, this will aggravate the condition. Some restraint is desirable by at least partially wrapping the cat in a rug or an old coat, and placing in a basket or a box.

Whatever the case of bleeding, as blood contains salt in appreciable amount, it is wise to **give frequent sips of saline solution** (a level teaspoon of table salt to a pint of water) and also fresh water with sugar or glucose added should be available nearby all the time, but do not give any food.

After all cases of bleeding there is excessive weakness. Rest and quiet and special nourishment are essential to regain strength. Keep the cat in a confined space, well wrapped and with a wrapped hot water bottle to lie on and protected from draughts. After 24 hours give frequent drinks of warm Lactol, weak soups, also add a little of Sherley's Lintox Tonic to each drink offered. When the cat is able to take food a little more solid, start with Sherley's Lactol Meal or Lactol Biscuits soaked in warm Lactol or milk.

Never give stimulants in cases of extensive bleeding.

BOWELS (Intestines) INFLAMMATION OF

This may be caused by cold, eating sharp bones, coccidiosis or bacterial infection, and in kittens it may be the result of worms. The disease may also result from stoppage of the bowels in cases of chronic constipation; hair-ball and irritant poisons generally cause inflammation of the bowels. It is often present also in cases of diarrhoea and dysentery.

Symptoms.—The abdomen may be hard and painful to the touch. Thirst is occasionally noted but sometimes water and food are refused. Acute cases are accompanied by a rise of temperature. The bowels may be constipated or there may be diarrhoea.

Treatment.—If there is diarrhoea give a dose of Sherley's Diarrhoea Cream. If the bowels are constipated give Lik-a-Med Laxative Cream, and if they do not operate after the laxative give an enema of warm soapy water—see p. 94. The enema must be repeated several times during the day until the bowels operate. Hot linseed-meal poultices should be applied to the abdomen.

A course of Creo-Garlic internal antiseptic pills will help to reduce internal infection.

Sharp bones of fish, fowl or rabbit are the most frequent cause of serious bowel inflammation therefore if the symptoms do not clear up in a few hours, seek veterinary advice.

117

BREAST INFLAMMATION (Mammitis or Mastitis)

Occasionally when a queen is suckling kittens there is more milk than they can take, or some teats may be neglected, the milk glands become swollen, hard, and very painful, the queen refuses food and lies on her side moaning. The breasts are swollen, red and tender. Abscesses may form if the breasts are not relieved as the secretion is mainly pus and if the abscesses develop and burst without proper attention nasty scars or lumps are left which can later become tumours. This may happen if all the kittens have been removed.

Treatment.—Urgent antibiotic treatment should be sought at once. Failing this the queen should be given a good dose of Lik-a-Med Laxative Cream and the breasts should be fomented with Antiphlogistine or Kaolin or if not available then bread poultice or hot water compresses, taking care to test the heat on the back of your hand to make sure it will not scald her. Repeat the foments three or four times a day. If there is great congestion, the milk, if any, must be drawn off from the affected glands night and morning. If an abscess forms treat as recommended for Abscesses. Kittens must be removed from the mother and hand-reared on Lactol (see page 43), or a foster-mother found.

See also page 144.

BRONCHITIS

This generally commences with a cold, cough, and difficulty in breathing. The cat sits up panting in bad cases, frequently coughing and wheezing and later followed by thick phlegm coughed up and sneezed from the nostrils. Sudden changes in temperature of the room or going outdoors may often cause these bronchial spasms.

Treatment.—Give a course of Creo-Garlic internal antiseptic Pills. The cat should be kept in an airy ventilated room with a warm temperature from 55 to 60 degrees Fahr. (13° to 16°C.) and a bronchitis kettle kept going, a piece of wool saturated with eucalyptus oil or a teaspoonful of Friar's Balsam being lightly packed in the spout of the kettle.

When the inhalations cannot be easily arranged, put the patient into a small room with a spirit lamp or paraffin heater and boil on it a kettle of water to which a teaspoonful of Friar's Balsam has been added, occasionally letting this simmer for a few hours at a time until breathing seems easier.

Keep to a light diet; no meat or fish for a few days. Cats that are overfed and become excessively fat are frequent victims of bronchial troubles in later life and require a reduced diet, preferably lean minced meat.

If the cat's temperature exceeds 102°F. (38.9°C.) a Veterinary Surgeon should be called in. Modern antibiotic treatment can often cut short an acute case in a few hours.

See also Asthma, Distemper, and Pneumonia.

BURNS

See also SCALDS

The common site of burns in a cat is along the spinal region, where sparks and cinders from a fire, or scalding water from a kettle, have fallen. These are usually classed as minor, i.e. first degree burns.

First degree burns affect the hair and skin surface.

Second and third degree burns are deeper and when affecting very large areas of the body the pain and shock can cause death.

FIRST AID in cases of Burns.

Exclude air from the burnt or scalded surfaces. Apply Carron Oil or Flavine Oil Emulsion or Tannic Acid Jelly, or even cold strong tea (of which tannic acid is a constituent), soaked on a **clean** pad or handkerchief. Then bandage with clean cloths to exclude all air. Every precaution should be taken to avoid the burns becoming septic.

If the burns are not very extensive, apply Sherley's Veterinary Ointment on a handkerchief. If sulphanilamide powder is available give a light dusting before the second dressing of ointment. Keep the cat warm and give plenty of water to drink. **The hair never grows on the skin that has been burned so deeply that the roots have been destroyed.**

FOR ACID BURNS—apply a solution of Bicarbonate of Soda (baking powder), one teaspoon per cup of water.

FOR ALKALI BURNS (Quicklime, etc.)—use vinegar and water 50/50.

In all extensive burns or scalds, Veterinary help is an urgent matter as an anaesthetic may be necessary for treatment, and shock is often an alarming accompaniment.

CANKER OF THE EAR (Otorrhoea)

Canker of the ear is a term generally used to denote various afflictions of the ear and is a chronic disease involving the auditory canal. Often there is an unpleasant-smelling discharge.

In the majority of cases the canker actually originates from the presence of the ear mange parasite which sets up intense irritation and later complications.

Other common afflictions of the ear are eczema, catarrh with a wax-like substance, inflammation of the cartilages of the ear and of the canal and its deeper structures. Wounds and bruises are often self-inflicted by the cat scratching itself to relieve the irritation and there may be a haematoma (" blood-blister ") in the ear flap. The use of strong irritant bathing solutions inside the ear can be very harmful too. In the summer months grass awns in the ear can be deeply embedded and these need to be removed by a veterinary surgeon. With the aid of a speculum he can examine the inner ear and ascertain the causes or remove any foreign bodies, if they are present.

Symptoms.—In Canker of the Ear there is acute irritation and the cat shakes its head, holds the head on one side, scratches frequently, and where the canker has been neglected and becomes very painful, the cat eventually hates to have his head or ears touched, whereas in the early stages of canker, he may like to have his ears rubbed.

When any ear trouble is noticed Sherley's Canker Lotion Capsules should be applied freely, one capsule in each ear and in the meantime if the cat is scratching excessively then every effort should be made to keep the cat from scratching the ear by applying a bandage or " gloves " on the cat's paws. See pages 129–131.

If there is a wet discharge from the ear, the mattery discharge should be swabbed away very carefully with cotton wool just slightly damped with diluted Amplexol, which is both antiseptic and deodorant. Burn the wool and wash the hands immediately. Do not endanger the hearing of your cat by poking around inside the ear with swabs, sticks, etc., and do not use any strong chemicals. Sherley's Canker Powder puffed into the ears will help to relieve even the very worst cases of wet canker and recurrences may be prevented by dusting a little of the Canker Powder into the ears two or three times a week.

In all cases of Ear Canker Sherley's Cooling Tablets are an excellent blood tonic.

CATARRH (Coryza—Influenza Cold)

Just as with humans, cats are very subject to infection by an assortment of viruses and also ills such as colds and influenza, usually the result of a chill or contracted from another cat suffering from a cold. This complaint is most contagious and if one cat starts in a cattery it generally runs through the whole lot.

The symptoms are frequent sneezing, a semi-watery discharge from nose and eyes, and often a dribbling from the mouth as a result of the throat being inflamed and sore. In many cases the cold is accompanied by a cough. As a rule there is little or no temperature, and if the cat is looked after and not allowed to go out it soon gets well, but if the patient is neglected and allowed to run in and out he or she may get a fresh chill and pneumonia may result, which is of course serious.

Treatment.—Give Sherley's Anti-Flu & Fever Tablets, also Lik-a-Med Laxative once only at onset of illness and continue with the tablets daily until the cat is quite well. Keep the cat indoors and supply a box of sand, cinders, or dry mould for sanitary purposes.

Cats with only a simple cold do not usually go off their food, and it is a good plan to let them have plenty of meat, which should be raw for choice, as it is more strengthening; if the appetite is indifferent they can be tempted with the various foods for invalids.

The difference between ordinary catarrh and feline distemper is that there is little or no fever (not more than about 102°F. (38.9°C.) with catarrh) whereas in distemper the temperature quickly rises to around 104°F. (40°C.). See Distemper, also Feline Enteritis.

CHOKING

Cats usually choke because of small sharp bones from fish, poultry, chops, rabbit, etc., and even from fish-hooks and needles which they swallow. These may become lodged across the upper jaw between the back teeth or in the throat or gullet. Often they are visible as soon as the mouth is opened and, if your cat will permit it, can be removed, preferably with a pair of blunt-nosed forceps rather than with the fingers. Even the gentlest of pets may bite when in pain. Otherwise, the task is best performed by a Veterinary Surgeon, who will give the cat sedation.

The symptoms of choking are " retching " (attempting to vomit) and refusing food . . . often also even refusing to drink. The cat may paw and claw at its mouth as if trying to remove something;

the gulping and the retching probably occurring at quite frequent intervals. If the object gets lodged between the upper and lower jaws then the mouth remains partly open and dribbling will also be an additional symptom. If the object is eaten during the feeding there may be a sudden shriek of pain, the cat backing away from the food, holding his head and neck outstretched.

Holding open the cat's mouth for examination and removal of the object is not an easy task and requires a separate person holding the cat, which should be well wrapped in a rug to prevent scratching. To open the mouth lift the top jaw from above with the first finger and thumb and hold down the lower jaw with a finger of the same hand. Then, if your cat is quite docile, extract the object with the finger and thumb of the other hand or with blunt-nosed forceps. See page 27.

Fish-hooks in the tongue or cheek cannot be pulled out because of the barb on the tip and may need to be pushed through the flesh after cutting off any catgut attached or, if the barb can be carefully snipped off with wire-cutting pliers—the barb being held so that this is not swallowed—then the rest of the hook can be pulled out. This also is best carried out under light anaesthesia by a Veterinary Surgeon.

COCCIDIOSIS.—See page 70, also Diarrhoea.

COLIC.—See Gripes.

CONJUNCTIVITIS.—See Eyes.

<h1 align="center">CONSTIPATION</h1>

A cat's motions should be formed and firm and passed regularly once or twice a day without any difficulty and without excessive straining. Many cats, particularly male doctored cats mainly confined to the house or flat are subject to constipation as a result of unsuitable or too much food and want of proper exercise. The stools may be so hard that the cat has difficulty in passing them.

In some cases it is so bad that the cat cries out when he attempts to relieve himself. There may be a spike of fish or other bone lodged in the lower bowel. **Constipation should never be allowed to continue,** lest real obstruction or stoppage of the bowels results. At the least it will make the parts very sore and tender. In some cases, more particularly long-haired breeds, the trouble may be caused by accumulation of hair. See Hair-Ball.

The condition is often easily avoided simply by giving an occasional dose of Sherley's Lik-a-Med Laxative—dabbed on the cat's nose or paw or on food—he licks it off with pleasure.

Castor oil should never be given as it causes griping and to some cats it acts almost like a mild poison.

Liquid Paraffin may be used **only occasionally and not continued** for more than a few days at a time as this reduces the nutritional benefits of the foods eaten.

Habitual constipation. If the cat has reasonable exercise and a varied diet then this may indicate some internal disorder and veterinary advice should be sought. Lik-a-Med Laxative may be given fairly regularly with absolute safety. It brings about an easy bowel action without in any way griping or upsetting the stomach. It is pleasant and may be given on to the nose from the tube or on a piece of biscuit or other food. Sherley-Vite Tablets, which contain vitamins, minerals and proteins, should be given daily and with correct diet plus a once-weekly dose of Lik-a-Med Laxative this complete treatment will in most cases correct habitual constipation. Your pet cat needs to be watched and the stools observed occasionally to make sure his bowels are in good order.

See Anus, also Enemas.

CONVULSIONS.—See Fits.

COUGHS

Cats may suffer from a cough due to one or more of a number of conditions or diseases . . . anything from a chill to feline distemper . . . but in long-haired breeds particularly, a common cause is Hair-Ball. This is a matted conglomeration of fur which has been licked off the coat and swallowed and becomes lodged in the stomach, gradually increasing in size. The cat then coughs frequently in its endeavours to expel the ball. The various causes of coughing are dealt with under the following headings . . . Asthma, Bronchitis, Broncho-Pneumonia, Chills and Colds, Tuberculosis, Worms.

Where a chill is suspected, early administration of Sherley's Anti-Flu & Fever Tablets can help to prevent more serious ills.

Whilst the patient is being treated for the true cause of the cough temporary relief may be obtained by giving honey to lick and Sherley's Creo-Garlic Pills as an internal antiseptic. However, the underlying cause of the coughing must be investigated.

CYSTITIS.—See Bladder.

CRYPTORCHIDISM (Hidden Testicle)

This is the failure of one or both of the testicles to descend into the scrotum (Cryptorchid—both testicles retained. Monorchid—one retained) and is not uncommon. They should have descended by the time male kittens are about 4 months old although sometimes this may be delayed 2 or 3 months more. The kitten should have veterinary attention if one or both testicles have not descended when 6 or 7 months of age.

A monorchid cat can be used for stud purposes, but not a cryptorchid. See also Stud Cats.

CYSTS

These are usually caused by some irritation and cats in particular are susceptible to cysts inside the ear flaps from scratching. These ear flap swellings are blood-blisters (haematoma) and unless carefully operated on to remove the blood clot causing the swelling, will result in puckering of the ear flap, and disfigurement. The initial cause may therefore be neglect of some irritation inside the ear, such as Canker, so easily prevented by an occasional puff with Sherley's Canker Powder.

Cyst-like growths or swellings may occur on the tongue and eye and also need expert veterinary attention. See also Abscesses, Tumours, and Ear.

DEAFNESS

Deafness is often found in white cats with blue eyes, when it is generally congenital and incurable. It also occurs in older cats as the result of neglected canker or an accumulation of wax in the ears. This latter condition may be relieved by pouring a few drops of slightly warmed glycerin or almond oil or olive oil or Sherley's Canker Lotion into the ears night and morning for a couple of days, and then cleansing them thoroughly with a solution prepared by mixing equal parts of warm water and methylated spirit. Dry the ear with cotton wool twisted round a small stick or between the prongs of a pair of small blunt-nosed tweezers **but do not poke around deep inside the ear** or the drum, which is at the far end of the passage, may be injured or even punctured. Great gentleness and some experience is required in dressing the ears. Syringing without professional guidance is not recommended.

Deafness sometimes follows gas poisoning and also vitamin deficiency for which latter Lintox Tonic and Sherley-Vite Tablets are invaluable.

Deafness may also be due to Canker, and disappears when the Canker is cured.

DIABETES

There are two types of Diabetes, D. Mellitus and D. Insipidus.

In *Diabetes Mellitus* the cat is extremely thirsty and the abdomen becomes swollen and hard in contrast to the rest of the body where wasting and emaciation occur. Large quantities of light-coloured urine are passed, which reveal the presence of sugar when tested.

The diet should consist mainly of meat. The surest treatment is the injection of insulin; therefore it is, of course, essential to take the cat to a veterinary surgeon.

Diabetes Insipidus produces similar symptoms to those of D. Mellitus but is characterised by the absence of sugar from the urine passed. It is usually the accompaniment of a serious illness, such as disease of the kidneys. Here again the cat must be taken to a veterinary surgeon.

DIARRHOEA

Diarrhoea often accompanies other diseases and cats and kittens may suffer from diarrhoea, often due to unsuitable foods; change of diet; indigestion; a chill; parasites such as coccidiosis; various illnesses such as distemper, tuberculosis, liver disease; vitamin A deficiency, etc. Diarrhoea is often caused by worms, particularly in kittens, and old cats sometimes suffer from chronic diarrhoea.

Eating from dirty food dishes which have been left uncovered and have become contaminated can also be possible causes.

The treatment of diarrhoea really depends upon the cause but in all cases it is advisable to clear out all possible irritant matter from the intestines by giving a dose of Sherley's Lik-a-Med Laxative, excepting in severe illnesses or fevers and also except to kittens under 3 months of age as in their case the diarrhoea is probably caused by worms. **After the Lik-a-Med has worked then give Sherley's Anti-Diarrhoea Cream according to the directions on the carton.**

If the diet is suspected change this at once and begin by fasting the cat for 24 hours then feed with a little fresh raw meat minced and mixed with Lactol Meal or Lactol Biscuits crumbled together, and a little warm milk added.

If the patient is a kitten and worms are suspected, treat with Sherley's Roundworm Tablets.

125

When the diarrhoea is of a persistent nature the Diarrhoea Cream may be repeated daily and also 2 drops of Chlorodyne may be given with each dose. The Chlorodyne needs to be given mixed with butter or honey—if necessary from a medicine dropper on to the tongue. See page 91.

Certain of the sulphonamide drugs, of which M & B 693 was a famous example, are used in certain kinds of diarrhoea.

If the rectum becomes sore, insert the smallest size Hamamelin (Witch Hazel) suppositories daily following bowel evacuation.

An excellent diet in cases of diarrhoea is Lactol mixed as for invalids but with arrowroot gruel instead of plain water; clear beef tea with isinglass is good in some cases, and chopped lean raw beef is sometimes better than anything, especially in cases of chronic diarrhoea, but no meat should be given if there is any blood and mucus with the motions.

To drink give either home-made barley water or white of egg in water or Lactol.

DISTEMPER—FELINE (Cat Influenza)

This is the principal catarrhal disease of the cat and like dog distemper it is caused by a virus but it is not infectious to dogs—nor is the virus of dog distemper infectious to cats.

Cat distemper is regarded by Veterinary Surgeons as being involved in most of the catarrhal conditions—colds, catarrh and influenza, met with in the cat—and is very different in its onset and course from the disease Feline Enteritis, although complications such as pneumonia or inflammation of other organs of the body can occur due to the weakened resistance to disease.

Distemper may occur at any age and, as so often happens with virus diseases in animals and man, appears to run in cycles—for some years it may be nothing worse than a severe cold, then there may be a season or a succession of years when the viruses have more severe and widespread effects, although fatalities from the distemper itself are rare in normally healthy cats.

The distemper virus is spread by infected cats sneezing or by contact or from the cat stepping in the droppings of nasal discharge of an infected cat and then cleaning itself. A healthy well-nourished cat living in the household is to some extent resistant to the virus. However, all cats are quickly infected if directly sneezed at by an infected cat—or if living in crowded quarters or pens with other cats near. It is important, therefore, that in catteries there should be plenty of air space around each pen and access to an open air cage and fresh air without draughts, at all times. Also any cat which sneezes must be isolated immediately to avoid widespread infection. Kittens are very susceptible to the infection.

In adult cats the symptoms usually appear about 5 days after contact with the infection, just like an influenza cold . . . sniffles, runny nose, sneezing and coughing, loss of appetite, and with a temperature of about 104°F. (40°C.). The cat appears dull and listless, lies belly-flat, loses weight, the eyes are heavy and only half open. Later the nasal discharge becomes thicker. In some cases there may be diarrhoea.

In kittens the symptoms and effects of the disease are very quickly seen and, in weaker kittens, may be fatal. **Patients must be kept in a separate room, warm and cosy,** and a moist atmosphere maintained by the steam from a kettle to which a teaspoonful of Friar's Balsam may be added to medicate the atmosphere and soothe the inflamed membranes of the throat and chest and clear the nasal passages. The eyes should be swabbed with diluted Sherley's Eye Lotion and the nose with Sherley's Antiseptic Lotion and all used dressings burned immediately. Drinks of warm Lactol with a little Lintox Tonic added are usually accepted but as cats with catarrh lose most of their sense of smell they will refuse food they cannot smell. However, when the cat is convalescent he will take something with a penetrating smell, such as sardines, or sardine oil put on Lactol Biscuits, or fish. Other light foods may be given later, with Lactol and glucose added for extra-special nourishment.

During the illness it is necessary to ensure that the bowels are functioning regularly and Lik-a-Med Laxative should be given— a small dose daily if necessary.

Infection can be passed on by the persons attending a sick cat so protect other cats from infection by wearing protective clothing—an old plastic raincoat, goloshes or gumboots, which can be washed over when leaving the sickroom and a shallow tray with about an inch of diluted Sherley's Antiseptic Lotion or Kennel Fluid should be near the door to rinse the soles of the feet free from any viruses that have become attached whilst in the sickroom.

The distemper virus can remain active for 2 or 3 months, therefore do not introduce a new cat or kitten where there has been a case of distemper until the premises have been thoroughly disinfected several times and until at least 3 months after the illness. See also Catarrh and Enteritis.

DROPSY AND ASCITES

Cats, like other animals, occasionally suffer from dropsy of the chest and also of the abdomen, the latter being called Ascites. These conditions are usually connected with some other internal condition and need veterinary attention to ascertain the cause and relieve the condition.

In Dropsy, which is the result of pleurisy and pneumonia, the symptoms are very distressed breathing, not so very quick but breathing with a great effort, the chest greatly expanding and the flanks having a kind of in and out movement. When the chest is very full of fluid and the breathing very bad the cat is unable to lie down but sits with the head up, nose poked out and breathing through the mouth.

Medicine is of little use but in both Dropsy of the Chest and Dropsy of the Abdomen (the latter known as Ascites) the fluid in the chest cavity can be removed by a Veterinary Surgeon and often brings enormous relief to the breathing.

Let the cat have any food which will be eaten voluntarily, but if food is refused then give Lactol or beef essence alternately every three hours, also ten drops of brandy in a teaspoonful of milk occasionally when the breathing is bad.

Ascites, or dropsy of the abdomen, is not of frequent occurrence, but cats do get it occasionally as the result of a diseased liver or diseased kidneys and from certain diseases of the heart. In these cases the abdomen is distended whilst the chest becomes thin, as also the neck and other parts, so much so that the bones may be easily felt under the skin. Breathing is quicker than normal. If after placing the hand on one side of the abdomen the opposite side is gently tapped with the fingers, the fluid is easily felt.

In a female cat with ascites it is sometimes incorrectly assumed that she is pregnant. As to treatment, it is important to get the bowels to operate freely, for which give Sherley's Lik-a-Med Laxative Cream. Also Sherley-Vite Tablets should be given twice a day.

When the abdomen becomes very distended so that the cat is unable to lie down and the breathing is very distressed, the cat may be greatly relieved by operation to draw off the fluid but in many cases relief is only temporary, for the fluid often quickly collects again. It is, however, worthwhile as many cats have been known to recover after this treatment. Injections of Mersalyl have proved of great value in dropsy.

These conditions may cause excessive thirst which tends to increase the collection of fluid; therefore, water intake should be limited in quantity, allowing just sufficient to quench the thirst from time to time.

A good nourishing easily digested protein diet is required and may consist of any foods which the cat will eat, which should include fresh raw meat with Lactol Biscuits and Liver Snaps in addition to fish once daily. Fifteen drops of unsweetened gin may also be given three times a day in a dessertspoonful of milk—this acts as a good appetiser and stimulates the kidneys.

DYSPEPSIA—See Indigestion.

EAR FLAP INJURIES

Haematoma.—Blood blisters inside the ear . . . and also outer ear scratches and injuries to the edge of the ear flap are not uncommon in cats. Sometimes they are caused by bruises as a result of fighting, or most commonly of all, self-inflicted in the cat's efforts to relieve the irritations of canker, etc., inside the ear.

In Haematoma the inside flap becomes greatly swollen and painful and the swelling contains blood serum and not pus. With head-shaking and scratching these tend to enlarge. If the swelling is very slight, not bigger than a broad bean, provided the cat does not bruise it by scratching with its paws it may be reabsorbed and only leave a slight crinkling of the ear as the fluid hardens and becomes partly absorbed. Very often, however, the ear swellings are quite large—as big as a walnut or even bigger—and in this case they require to be lanced by a Veterinary Surgeon in order that the contained blood clot may drain away freely and completely. If there is no veterinary service available then lancing, preferably under sedation, needs to be as follows:

Haematoma—usually the result of a bruise. With a sterilised surgical knife (scalpel) open the swelling freely on the inside of the flap, at lowest part when the ear is in its natural position, so that all the fluid (which is blood serum) may run out. After the cavity is quite empty the wound should be plugged with a piece of surgical ribbon gauze smeared over with Veterinary Ointment; **if the wound is not kept open in this way for about three days fluid will collect again.** Change the gauze twice a day. The ear canal should also be attended to, as in these cases the irritation is usually due to infestation with ear mites. See Canker.

In external injuries to edge and back of flap.—Clip away the hair from around the injury and cleanse with diluted Sherley's Antiseptic Lotion daily and apply Veterinary Ointment. If the wound constantly re-opens because it is rubbed and scratched then a leather helmet may be necessary.

Deep wounds may need stitches to facilitate healing.

With cats, it is not at all easy to arrange dressings so that no deforming of the ear occurs as a result of the injury, and the ear should be kept at rest by making the cat wear a cap, as illustrated.

Pattern for cap. To be made of linen.

ECLAMPSIA

This is the condition of collapse and convulsions occasionally occurring with milk fever when a queen is in the later stages of pregnancy, or just after. Eclampsia is due to a calcium deficiency, remedied quickly by injections of soluble calcium salts given by your Veterinary Surgeon. It may often be avoided by feeding regularly with Lactol every day, the Vitamin D content helping the assimilation of the calcium and phosphorus from food. See also Fits and Milk Fever.

ECZEMA

It is not always easy to diagnose the cause of Eczema in cats because many types of skin troubles are due to either fungi (as in ringworm), mites (as in mange), maggots, lice, fleas, etc., most of which are contagious or spread by infestation, and any skin troubles in kittens are usually due to some parasite.

Eczema, however, is not contagious but there is a very common type of eczema that occurs only in adult male neutered cats which does tend to recur unless the particular cause can be diagnosed and either corrected or treated and often this is a case of " trial and error ". Skin scrapings can often help to confirm a diagnosis.

The symptoms of Eczema are red and inflamed patches varying in size from an inch to 3 or 4 inches across and neglected patches become mattery as a result of the cat constantly licking them. The most common parts to be affected are the back, the belly, inside the thighs, and the tail, but any part may become attacked. It seldom spreads to the head or face, which it would do if it were contagious, as the cat, in continually licking the affected parts, is always rubbing her face against them.

Treatment.—The great thing if possible is to prevent the cat from constantly licking the places as the rough tongue prevents healing. To stop the licking make the cat wear a wide cardboard collar, made as depicted; the patient may not like it at first, but soon becomes accustomed to it, and the places then heal quickly with the following treatment.

The places that are at all mattery should be cleaned with Amplexol diluted with warm water and applied with swabs of cotton-wool. Afterwards gently dry with a piece of soft rag like an old but clean handkerchief and then dab the parts freely with Sherley's Skin Cure or Sherley's Eczema and Mange Lotion. Repeat twice a day. These lotions may also be applied around the mouth but not around the eyes. A cat suffering from eczema should always be treated for worms as eczema cannot be cured whilst a cat is affected with worms.

Cats that are over-fat, or in a poor and thin condition should have a course of Sherley-Vite Tablets, as eczema is often the result of anaemia and any cat subject to eczema should be given Sherley-Vites regularly during the Spring and Summer. These will often prevent an attack.

Diet.—A cat fed mainly on starchy foods may benefit on a more meaty diet . . . or too much fish may be the cause, in fact a completely fish diet will cause eczema in most cats. Even a change to dog biscuits, wholemeal bread, Lactol Biscuits and Liver Snaps will often bring about a cure. **Therefore . . . if your cat has been living mainly on starchy foods change to meat . . . if on fish then change to meat.**

In all skin diseases the golden rules are . . . (1) Check for the presence of parasites, particularly fleas, and treat these. (2) If no parasites are present, then change to another type of food.
(3) Give just one Sherley-Vite tablet each day.
See the Diet Chart on pages 19–21 and 98–99.

131

ENTERITIS—INFECTIOUS FELINE

Also known as—**Infectious Gastro-Enteritis,
Specific Feline Enteritis,** etc.; and in the U.S.A. as **Panleucopenia**

**Infectious Enteritis is quite different from Feline Distemper
and quite distinct in its symptoms.**

Infectious Enteritis is the oldest known disease of the cat and
there is a clear record of it described in the 15th century. It is
caused by a microscopic virus and is extremely infectious and
fatal; often all the cats in the neighbourhood have died in a few
days of each other and the impression sometimes arises that
someone is indulging in poisoning.

Infectious Enteritis is met with more often in young cats than
old. Siamese and Persian cats are particularly affected and become
dangerously ill with it. The summer months July and August are
the common months for epidemics to appear.

**The disease comes on suddenly with rise in temperature, at first
up to 105°F. (40.6°C.) and then falling to 103°F. (39.4°C.). The
cat refuses food, sits huddled up with head down and shows a tendency
to sit over a water bowl or sink but does not drink any water.
Occasionally it vomits a frothy brown mucus and shows signs of
pain in so doing.** It may cry slightly when you pick it up or when the
abdomen is touched, as if it is tender and painful. Blood-stained
motions are occasionally noticed. Collapse with a falling temperature occurs within 48 hours but death may be as quick as only a
matter of a few hours from the observance of the first symptom.

The period of incubation from the time of infection from another
cat is about 2 to 4 days and it can be caught by direct contact as
well as through flies, from vessels, beds, clothing, etc.

Without proper treatment rarely do more than 20 per cent of
affected animals survive, and those which do recover need to be
well nourished on Lactol and easily digested broths. Those cats
which do recover from Infectious Enteritis have a life-long
immunity from this particular disease.

Treatment is an urgent matter and should be entrusted to a
Veterinary Surgeon immediately. In catteries and breeding
establishments it is good to know now that an efficient vaccine is
available which will protect cats from accidental infection
provided they are injected before they leave their homes to board out.

In a cattery.—Any affected cats must be isolated immediately
and all pens disinfected and flies exterminated. Persons attending
the sick must keep away from all other cats on the premises, or

if necessary to handle the other cats then every precaution taken to avoid carrying infection—as described on pages 100–102.

So far as nursing is concerned, before the Veterinary Surgeon arrives keep the cat wrapped up with warm hot water bottles under the blanket and give sips of glucose water every now and then. The cats get extremely dehydrated, which means that loss of fluid in the body tissues takes place, and as far as possible this should be replaced by drinking water. This may have to be done by the Veterinary Surgeon injecting glucose saline together with other drugs he may use to cure the animal.

Cats and kittens can and should be immunised by having innoculations carried out by the Veterinary Surgeon and are thereby free from any risk of this infection. See also Gastritis.

THE EYE

Cats are not very subject to diseases of the eye but they do occasionally become injured as the result of fighting or from other causes, and the cornea—the front or window of the eye, may become lacerated. In such cases the eye should be bathed with Sherley's Eye Lotion diluted with a little warm boiled water, applied to the eye with a good-sized wad of cotton-wool—not a sponge, as this quickly becomes fouled. Discard the wool after each application and always burn used dressings. As soon as the inflammation has cleared, it is advisable to apply Golden Eye Ointment twice a day; this will promote healing and help to remove the cloudiness of the cornea.

Cases occur where the third eyelid, which is a membranous structure called the **Nictitating Membrane or Haw** remains partially over the front of the eye. This third eyelid is normally concealed by the lower eyelid and acts as nature's pocket handkerchief, coming up from the inner side of the lower lid for the removal of any foreign body which may enter the eye. When this third eyelid is partly over the eye for long periods or frequently, it is usually an indication that the cat is ill—often the indication of stomach upset or intestinal parasites rather than any eye disease and it may even be caused by the cat being allowed to sit and gaze into the fire.

If the cat is in reasonably good condition then a course of Sherley-Vite Tablets will help to bring the cat back into perfect condition. After weakening diseases or severe injury, however, it is not uncommon for the third eyelid to remain closed permanently over half the eye, causing partial mechanical blindness and this would then have to be removed by a Veterinary Surgeon.

133

COLD IN THE EYE

The white of the eye and also the lining of the eyelid become red from inflammation, the eyes run with tears and later often with thin matter. The third eyelid at the inner corner of the eye is pushed forward and partly covers over that part of the eye and some people think that the cat is going blind, but this is seldom the case. Treat the eyes the same as in the previous paragraph.

EYE INJURIES AND FOREIGN MATTER

If only one eye is affected then this is most likely due to some foreign body (perhaps a small piece of metal embedded in the eye, which the Veterinary Surgeon can remove with an electro-magnet) or a scratch, or conjunctivitis.

If both eyes are inflamed and with tears or thin matter, then it is more likely to be a cold or the early signs of cat distemper.

Examine the eye to ascertain the cause, if possible, and treat as above with the eye lotion and ointment and if there is no improvement within one or, at the most, two days, then consult the Veterinary Surgeon.

In the case of both eyes being inflamed and with tears or matter and accompanied by sneezing and the possibility of distemper, during the intervening period the further symptoms of distemper will by then have appeared. See Distemper, also Cysts.

EYE-DISLOCATION

This is not uncommon in cats, as also in dogs with prominent eyes such as Pekes and Pugs. The eye comes right out of the socket on the cheek, projecting beyond the lids and to save the sight the dislocated eye must be immediately returned. The cat should be hurried to a Veterinary Surgeon, as an anaesthetic may be necessary and also in some cases perhaps, minor surgery. In the meantime keep the eye moist with a few drops of salad oil or olive oil.

Where veterinary or experienced help is not available, provided sedation by injection or anaesthesia is available (as without this the cat would be uncontrollable due to the intense pain), the treatment is as follows . . . First thoroughly clean the eye by allowing a stream of warm water to run over it from above downwards; if any boracic acid is at hand add a teaspoonful to each pint of water. Pour a few drops of salad oil or olive oil around the base of the eye, and with a clean folded handkerchief then apply pressure with the fingers to the front of the eye, gently pulling the eyelids over the globe as the pressure is applied, when it will usually slip back into place. A fair amount of pressure is sometimes required before the eye will go back, and this may be safely applied without fear of rupturing the organ. The only after-treatment required is to bathe the eye two or three times a day with Sherley's Eye Lotion.

EYE—FILM OVER (BLUE EYE)

Opacity of the Cornea (Keratitis)

This condition is generally the result of an injury and in such cases the cornea or front of the eye is usually torn. See the preceding sections on Injuries etc.

Treatment. At first, when the eye is painful and much inflamed, it should be fomented with warm diluted Sherley's Eye Lotion, as warm as you can stand on the back of your hand, for about ten minutes several times a day, using a swab of absorbent cotton-wool. It is not necessary to make it fresh each time provided you keep it covered, and only needs to be heated up. Otherwise, if the inflammation subsides quickly, follow with applications of Golden Eye Ointment twice a day. If however there appears to be much injury to the eye then veterinary attention is desirable.

In all eye troubles it is advisable to keep the cat away from very bright light and, if your cat will wear it, a leather or thick cardboard collar can be made somewhat like a lamp-shade with the purpose of preventing the cat from rubbing the eyes with its paws, somewhat as illustrated on page 131.

FITS AND CONVULSIONS

Fits are not common in cats, but they do occasionally suffer with them, more particularly kittens, either as the result of worms, or when changing their teeth (that is from four to six months of age), or anaemia (see below). Persians and Siamese kittens are more inclined to have fits than the ordinary short-haired breeds. Fits in adult cats may follow after any disease affecting the nervous system or inflammation of the brain (Encephalitis), or fright, or even severe canker if followed by rupture of the ear-drum.

Symptoms.—The patient, when apparently quite well, falls suddenly over on its side, struggles and kicks violently with its legs, champs the jaws, and frothy saliva comes from the mouth. This condition lasts less than half a minute, when the cat jumps up and rushes off, knocking itself against walls or anything else with which it comes in contact.

Do not attempt to hold a cat when in a fit without strong gloves as it can bite really hard and dangerously when it is out of its mind, as it is on these occasions. The best way to catch a cat in a fit is to throw a big cloth over it, and then, holding the back of the neck and the body, it can be safely picked up and placed in a basket where it should remain until it quietens down—a cold sponge held on the head often helps. Once a cat has had a fit there is always the chance of its having others unless some sedative medicine is given. Therefore, directly the cat can be handled give one Sherley's Sedative Tablet, which may be dissolved in a dessertspoonful of sweetened water or milk, and soon after give a dose of Lik-a-Med Laxative. The Sedative Tablets should be given for a week or longer, half a tablet three times a day. Also dose for worms . . . Tapeworm Tablets for adult cats . . . Round-worm Tablets for Kittens, after a lapse of 24 hours. Where excessive infestation of worms has been the cause once the animal is clear of the worms the fits usually cease.

Diet.—The diet should be light. Avoid meat; give fish, also plenty of milk or, better still, Lactol and Lactol Biscuits, and milk puddings with a teaspoonful of Sherley's Energol well stirred in . . . or Lactol Meal mixed in hot milk or Lactol, and given when lukewarm.

If the fits persist then it is advisable to consult a Veterinary Surgeon, informing him what treatment has been given.

See also Apoplexy, Anaemia, Canker, Worms.

FRACTURES (FIRST AID)

Cats usually manage to land safely on their feet even from great heights—except when in a panic, being chased by another cat, etc.—but in these days of heavy motor traffic they are sometimes panic-stricken and get bumped or run over on the road. Knocks by a car bumper can cause injury or fracture to the spine or hind-quarters, often followed eventually by some form of paralysis. Being run over by a wheel can cause leg or other fractures. A heavy weight falling on the back may fracture the spine. If the cat's tail is shut in a door the tail can be fractured.

Remember that in handling an injured cat, unless it is at least semi-conscious it will be frightened and in pain and dangerous to handle, therefore thick gloves should be worn or the cat held under a heavy cloth or coat.

Apart from **Greenstick Fractures** which may occur in all young animals—usually due to weakness of bone from diet deficiency in the mother—and are cracks across one side of the bone rather than of the complete bone—the two main types are . . .

Simple Fracture in which the bones are broken clean across, but without any external wound.

Compound Fractures, where bones are broken and the skin is lacerated, often with the broken ends of the bones exposed.

Most fractures of limbs do well after setting, but this is of course an experienced job, often calling for X-ray pictures of the fractures and for anaesthesia during the operation of setting the bones in the splints. The first objective is to get the cat to a Veterinary Surgeon as quickly as possible. Move the cat carefully—in a blanket holding the corners and then on a firm board to make an improvised stretcher.

If any fracture of a limb is apparent or suspected, handle the limb as little as possible. Keep the cat warm. **Apply a splint to immobilise the limb until the Veterinary Surgeon is reached or arrives.** A splint may be improvised with a flat piece of wood, cardboard or metal (if metal cover the edges with adhesive tape to avoid scratching), and the pieces should be long enough to reach well above and well below the fracture. Any open wound should be bathed with Sherley's Antiseptic Lotion diluted with warm water, then covered with clean lint or a clean handkerchief. Wrap the whole limb well in thick cotton-wool, then apply the splint and fix in position with two tapes around the limb, the splint tied above and below the fracture. Then bandage firmly, the whole length of the limb. A couple of turns of adhesive tape at the upper end, half on the bandage and half on the hair above, prevents the cotton bandage slipping.

In fractures of the ribs, if there is no haemorrhage, then there may be no internal injury, and complete rest may be sufficient. In any event, however, lay the animal on its injured side. If lung injury is present immediate veterinary attention is essential. Cold water pads may be applied in all cases of injured ribs.

In fractures of the tail, often caused by a closing door, there will be pain and swelling and the injured part of the tail may hang in an unusual position. Treat any external wound and then arrange a suitable splint in the same fashion as for fractured limbs.

See also Wounds.

GASTRITIS

The ordinary simple form of gastritis or inflammation of the stomach is not uncommon, and can be treated as indicated below, but it is important to differentiate between the simple gastritis and the contagious feline gastro-enteritis. The latter results in a high rate of mortality and this more serious disease is often first shown by symptoms which are identical with those indicating the presence of simple gastritis, but the more serious symptoms appear quite quickly if the illness is of the infectious type.

Ordinary Gastritis may occur as the result of a chill or eating small bones of birds or rabbits, also from eating putrid meat, and very frequently from worms, but it is wise to isolate cats with any form of gastritis away from other cats, and if the temperature rises much above 102.5°F. (39.2°C.) then the more serious disease Feline Enteritis must be suspected. See page 132.

The symptoms of ordinary gastritis are sickness, thirst and refusal of food—any food taken is soon vomited.

In ordinary cases a good dose of Sherley's Lik-a-Med Laxative should be given immediately. (Do not give castor oil as this may cause " gripes " and acts like a mild poison to some cats and kittens). About one hour after the laxative has been given commence dosing the cat with Sherley's Gastrine Tablets: one may be given every two or three hours, mixed in with a little glucose or sugar but not with anything fatty. Do not let the cat drink water. There is no hurry to give any food, in fact the cat is best without any food for some hours, and then strained beef essence may be offered. Cats are usually very fond of this but if it is refused give it from an egg spoon. This nourishment may be given every two or three hours. When the vomiting has ceased for about 24 hours, the cat can be offered some raw mutton, finely minced, and Lactol. Mutton is the most easily digested meat. See also Enteritis, Poisons, Worms, and Foods for Invalids.

GINGIVITIS.—See Teeth and Pyorrhoea.

GOITRE

Goitre is a swelling generally appearing on both sides of the front of the neck, due to the enlargement of the thyroid glands. It is usually seen in weak kittens and believed by some to be connected with iodine deficiency in the mother whilst pregnant. See also Eclampsia.

Treatment depends upon the cause. A course of iodine therapy or thyroid extract may be advised by the Veterinary Surgeon.

GRIPES OR COLIC

This is mainly confined to kittens from about 4 to 6 weeks of age onwards; it may be the result of indigestion, but as a rule it is caused by worms. The kitten is restless, crying and whining, and even howling if the pain is severe. The stomach is tucked up and the muscles feel hard and rigid. The attack is often accompanied by severe vomiting and diarrhoea. See Bowel.

Three or four drops of brandy in a teaspoonful of warm water will generally give relief, but in bad cases 2 drops of Chlorodyne in a teaspoonful of water should be given. Repeat in an hour if necessary, also give a dose of Lik-a-Med Laxative as soon as the severe symptoms have passed, or a dose of worming medicine if required. When the pain is very severe a flannel wrung almost dry out of boiling water and applied to the abdomen will usually give relief. Remember the possibility that the bowel may be obstructed and need surgical relief, so do not delay if there is no improvement in a few hours.

HAIR-BALL

This is an accumulation of hair in the stomach or bowels, **particularly in the long-haired breeds,** as the result of constantly licking the coat whilst it is being shed. The correct prevention is, of course, brushing and combing at least once a day and, in fact, as frequently as possible each day during moulting. Normally the cat will eat grass if it is available, causing itself to vomit up any hairs swallowed. If, however, the accumulated mass of hair is too large to be expelled this becomes quite a solid indigestible mass which cannot be passed through the bowel, increasing in size, setting up inflammation which may become absorbed into the whole of the cat's system. The hair-ball may be the size of a tennis ball.

The effects of hair-ball could be as simple as flatulence and bad breath, which can both be minimised by giving combined doses of Sherley's Gastrine Tablets and Amplex Veterinary Tablets, but these early stages can develop into serious weakness, loss of appetite and with a high temperature until the hair-ball is passed. **If the hair-ball is allowed to become excessively large then a surgical operation may be necessary.**

A dose of Sherley's Lik-a-Med Laxative given once weekly, particularly during the moulting season, will prevent the accumulation of hair-ball and in severe cases also give a tablespoonful of olive oil (from a sardine tin would do) or liquid paraffin, to help lubrication of the passage, about 3 or 4 hours before giving the Lik-a-Med, when a double dose of the laxative may be given. If this fails then an enema may be tried. Remember . . . **prevention is best, by frequent grooming plus a once-weekly dose of Lik-a-Med Laxative Cream.**

HEART DISEASE AND FAINTING

Cats suffering from valvular heart disease may, when excited, fall over on their side in a faint; they are quite unconscious for a short time, and on getting up look about in a dazed way for a few minutes, after which they appear all right and as though nothing had happened. Another faint may not occur for some time, but in bad cases the attacks are frequent.

Treatment.—In ordinary fainting attacks lay the cat out on the ground if possible with the head lower than the rest of the body. This helps circulation of blood to the brain. Apply smelling salts to the nose. Avoid exertion after meals and also prevent the cat getting excited. When the fainting occurs only very occasionally it is not worth while giving medicine, but if it is at all frequent it is best to consult a Veterinary Surgeon.

Diet.—Avoid overloading the stomach—a diet of very underdone meat with a little dry Lactol Biscuit or Lactol Meal is the best.

HEATSTROKE

This is unusual in cats, except where kept in enclosures exposed to hot sunshine without access to shade. Breathing appears heavy and the temperature very high. The cat may vomit, stagger and finally collapse.

Place the cat in the shade and apply cold water or cold cloths to the head, neck and shoulders. A few drops of brandy in cold water may be given to drink.

On recovery give a dose of Lik-a-Med Laxative.

HERNIA OR RUPTURE

This protrusion of a part beneath the skin from the abdominal cavity, usually the bowel, most commonly found at the navel where it is called **umbilical hernia,** is seldom seen in cats. It may be disregarded as long as it remains small and soft, as it often passes away in time.

Inguinal hernia shows itself as a swelling in the groin, most often on the left side, and female cats suffering from this should not be used for breeding until after an operation has been performed to remedy the condition as there may otherwise be serious complications.

Scrotal hernia is not common in cats. It is recognised by a soft swelling in the scrotum, which extends along the groin. It varies in size but is generally larger after a meal.

The only treatment for rupture is an operation by a Veterinary Surgeon and (except in the case of a minor umbilical hernia) it should always be performed, but not as a rule before the age of 3 months.

HICCOUGH

Cats and kittens sometimes suffer with hiccough, generally the result of indigestion caused either by worms or by some indigestible food. As a rule it is not serious and generally passes off in a short time, but if the animal has it very often then the treatment for worms should be carried out.

Sherley's Gastrine Tablets crumbled and mixed with milky water are often helpful. In very bad cases where the cat cannot get any rest from pain and the spasms continue for some time, Chlorodyne should be given—from one to two drops (according to size) in a teaspoonful of water. An occasional dose of Lik-a-Med Laxative helps, and the quantity of food should be reduced.

INDIGESTION (Dyspepsia)

The cat is occasionally sick after eating and sometimes in the morning before taking food, bringing up white frothy mucus. He is thirstier than usual, often drinking a large quantity of water. His tongue loses its natural moist state and pink colour and becomes dry and coated. There may be diarrhoea or constipation; he may suffer from wind and be dull and listless.

Treatment.—Alternate 3 hourly doses of Sherley's Gastrine Tablets and Cooling Tablets will do much to relieve your cat's indigestion, but before treating for indigestion however, the cat must be entirely freed from worms.

Diet.—Give raw minced meat, preferably mutton, with a few dry, broken-up Lactol Biscuits. Food should be given in small quantities three times a day. In very bad cases feeding entirely on Lactol (mixed as for invalids) for a time, greatly accelerates recovery. In elderly cats indigestion (dyspepsia) may be due to trouble with the teeth and difficulty in adequate chewing of the food, and regular Lactol with Lactol Meal are ideal in such cases. Energol granules may be given mixed in with all liquid or solid foods. See also Gastritis.

INFLUENZA.—See Distemper.

JAUNDICE

Jaundice is not so common amongst cats as in dogs (the latter pick up infection from rats) but it is occasionally seen in cases of organic disease of the liver, like cancer, also from pressure of other abdominal tumours on the bile duct, and it also occurs in tuberculosis. Jaundice in cats can follow catarrhal inflammation of the bowel with consequent blocking of the flow of bile into the intestine. The bile inflammation occurring in both distemper and infectious enteritis can lead to this type of jaundice, but far more often it is caused by the rat and mouse-borne infection called Leptospirosis. It is not, however, commonly met with in cats, which seem to have a much greater immunity to this infection than do dogs.

The principal symptom of jaundice is the turning yellow of the skin in light coloured and white animals, also inside the ears, the membrane lining the mouth, and the whites of the eyes, the colour increasing in density as the disease progresses until at last it is almost orange. In all instances beside the discoloration of the skin, etc., there is loss of appetite, constipation, and the cat gets very thin. This is more particularly the case when there is some organic disease of the liver such as cancer or tuberculosis, and when it is the result of these causes treatment is useless, and it is best to put the poor animal painlessly to sleep—see page 103.

When the disease is due to a cold or accompanying distemper

it is important to get the bowels to operate, and a dose of Sherley's Lik-a-Med Laxative should be given at once. Keep the cat in a nice dry warm room and apply hot **dry** flannels around the body.

Certain forms of jaundice in pets can be transmitted to humans therefore rubber gloves should be worn and all utensils and clothes disinfected, when nursing patients.

As to diet, cats, like dogs, will not take much food when suffering from this complaint, but will often be persuaded to drink a little glucose water at frequent intervals to combat dehydration (lack of water in the tissues). However, if food is still refused, very weak beef tea or other soup without any fat in it can be given in small quantities, although a special small feeding spoon may be necessary. When making beef tea or soup for cases of jaundice, green vegetables cooked with either of them is a good plan, but must be strained before being given. When the patient commences to feed itself, let it have boiled fish.

It is most important to get the bowels to operate in these cases, and if there is difficulty regarding this an enema of one teaspoonful of glycerin mixed with two tablespoonsful of warm water or a soapy enema should be given, using an enema syringe.
See page 94.

KIDNEY TROUBLES (Nephritis)

Cats, unlike dogs, are not much subject to diseases of the kidneys (Nephritis) but both sexes are liable to get congestion of the kidney as a result of some infection such as Leptospirosis mentioned in the above section on Jaundice. In such cases, there is seldom any trouble in passing the urine, but it is often blood-stained, and the cat passes water more frequently than usual. The treatment in these cases is to give one to two grains (50 to 100 mg.) of Hexamine three times a day. Many cats will take this in a small saucerful of milk, but if necessary it should be mixed with a teaspoonful of sweetened milk or water and poured down the throat. See Administering Medicine.

In all kidney and bladder troubles avoid meat, and feed on a diet of fish. The cat should also be encouraged to drink a lot of milk—the more the better—or water if it is preferred, so as to wash out the kidneys, and this is particularly necessary when the cat is inclined to suffer from gravel. It is also important to keep the bowels well opened, if necessary giving occasional doses of Sherley's Lik-a-Med Laxative Cream.

In cases of tuberculosis (now rare in Britain and in many other countries where strict inspection of cattle is carried out), if the kidneys become affected this condition is incurable and the cat should be put to sleep.

LUMBAGO.—See Rheumatism.

Lumbago is a form of rheumatism affecting the loins.

LUNGS.—See Pneumonia.

MANGE.—See Parasites.

MAMMITIS (also known as Mastitis)

This is inflammation of the milk glands and may occur in queens when all the litter has been taken away early and destroyed.

The inflammation may also occur in one or more of the glands as a result of some injury, or even if scratched by the kittens at the weaning stage.

Abscesses containing pus may form at one or two breasts along the teat line, when hot fomentations and eventual lancing may be necessary, but drugs of the penicillin family given early may completely arrest the attack.

Loss of milk whilst the kittens are tiny will call for provision of a foster-mother, or hand-rearing on Lactol.

In mammitis the bowels should be kept open, for which an occasional dose of Lik-a-Med may be given.

See Abscesses, Breeding, Eclampsia and Milk Fever.

MILK FEVER (Puerperal Eclampsia)

As mentioned briefly on page 130, Eclampsia is a condition of unsteadiness, then collapse, followed by convulsions, often similar to epileptic or fainting fits.

Puerperal Eclampsia is a condition due to a calcium drain on the system of the mother during lactation and this is quickly remedied by veterinary injections of soluble calcium salts.

144

This condition usually arises in cats which have lacked a calcium-forming diet during pregnancy and occurs whilst the cat is in the later stages of pregnancy or soon after the birth. It is usually due to the terrific strain upon her own resources and the draining of calcium from her system into the formation of the kittens. Milk Fever can occur also in a young cat which has been mated at her very first season—an important reason why first-season matings are unwise.

It is important to obtain veterinary help as quickly as possible —immediate injections can often save where the kittens or the mother may otherwise be lost.

Nevertheless prevention is best. During pregnancy and whilst nursing the kittens, Lactol is an essential part of the diet. The Vitamin D content of Lactol helps the queen to assimilate the necessary calcium and phosphorus for good bone formation in the kittens without draining her own body resources, and also ensures good natural milk supply for suckling the kittens. Lactol should be fed regularly to all queens in kitten and whilst suckling .... in addition to meals which include meat .... and one Sherley-Vite tablet a day provides essential vitamins.

See Care of the Queen, Fits, also Breast.

NERVOUSNESS

Nervousness in cats arises from many causes. Most cats are naturally nervous due to hereditary characteristics and show fright at different noises, others may run away or hide when visitors arrive . . . or refuse to enter a car. Such characteristics, when exaggerated, may be due to some connected accident or fright or to some ailment or condition of pain such as, for example, rheumatism or ear canker, with a fear of being handled on the painful part. If the cause can be diagnosed the problem can perhaps be overcome or at least understood . . . if not then Sherley's Sedative Tablets can be given to soothe the abnormal fears.

SHERLEY'S MILK SUPPRESSION TABLETS

For conditions where kittens or puppies have had
to be taken away—or in cases of 'false pregnancy'

NETTLERASH (Urticaria)

Generally the result of some allergy due to eating some unsuitable food—certain tinned foods—and sometimes perhaps caused by stinging nettles or insect bites, for example flea bites, on abnormally tender skin.

Swollen patches suddenly appear on the skin, in one part, or all over the body. If the ears are affected they may become nearly half-an-inch thick, and in other cases the cat is temporarily blind owing to the swollen condition of the eyelids. As a rule nettlerash passes off quickly with proper treatment, but it is liable to recur once a cat has had it, and will then sometimes be brought on by indigestion.

During an attack keep the cat warm and quiet, and give a dose of Lik-a-Med Laxative to be followed by Energol well mixed in with milk or Lactol, which should be continued for a few days after the nettlerash has gone. Give Sherley's Cooling Tablets to cool and purify the blood. If the diet is mainly fish then this should be changed, and in fact, the diet for a time should be light, mainly milky food such as Lactol Meal or Biscuits soaked in Lactol.

PARALYSIS

This is uncommon in cats but where it does occur is usually due to some injury of the spine such as being run over or some heavy object having fallen on the back of the cat, when usually the hind legs are affected.

Early veterinary examination is advisable . . . as soon as possible after the injury . . . or as soon as the infirmity is noticed. (See also Arthritis and Rheumatism).

PNEUMONIA

Pneumonia (inflammation of the lungs) is in most cases the result of a chill and often occurs during attacks of distemper.
The symptoms generally noticeable are: —

Very quick, distressed and obviously painful breathing.

An occasional coughing, due to the solids in the lung, and as the coughing clears this upwards the condition is somewhat easier (in some cases there is no cough at all, which is a bad sign).

A rise in temperature perhaps to 104°F. (40°C.). Tenderness on pressure to the chest. The cat is dull and listless and off its food.

Treatment.—To bring the temperature down give one or two Sherley's Fever Tablets, according to size, and then, **where it is possible, in all cases of pneumonia, the patient should be taken at once to a Veterinary Surgeon.** The tablets should be regarded only as a stop-gap as the Veterinary Surgeon will be able to give treatment with the modern antibiotics which, if given early, may ward off the attack altogether and prevent a long and painful illness.

If possible put the cat in a jacket—as illustrated—and line that part of the jacket which covers the sides of the chest with a double layer of white lint. A sleeve of an old woollen cardigan or jumper will do; cut holes in this for the front legs to go through. If the cat seems cold in normal room temperature this extra warmth is a great help. Do **not** use any liniment or strong embrocations. In very bad cases, if your cat will permit, it is a good plan to wring out the lint (which should be about three inches wide) in tepid water—wringing until almost dry; then place it round the cat's chest and cover this with a piece of plastic sheet, taking care that this well overlaps the lint. Keep them in place with the jacket arranged to fit rather tightly, but not so tight as to interfere with the breathing. Keep the patient in a warm but well-ventilated room . . . fresh air without any draught is important.

Pattern of coat, to be made of flannel.

POISONS
VERMIN POISONS, WEEDKILLERS
SLUG AND INSECT BAITS
SPRAYS OR POWDERS USED IN HORTICULTURE

Thanks to their careful eating habits cats are very rarely poisoned. If a cat develops symptoms such as vomiting, diarrhoea or lassitude (all of which might in other animals suggest some form of poisoning) one should **bear in mind the diseases of distemper and feline gastro-enteritis, the effects of which in some ways closely resemble poisoning.**

Accidental poisoning is however possible if a cat has eaten a rat or a mouse which contains enough of a poison in the intestines for the cat to be affected if it swallows the rat or mouse. Severe poisons containing either the virus which gives these pests a fatal disease, or phosphorus or some other organic poison, are sometimes laid down to destroy rats and mice. Fortunately however the newer drug for exterminating these pests, Warfarin, is not normally in palatable form for cats and is less likely to poison larger animals such as the cat. It would make it sick, but would need to eat quite a few doses to have any serious results.

Lead poisoning may occur after a room or building has been painted. Even turpentine evaporating from the painted surfaces and inhaled can be poisonous to some cats. Also, a cat can quickly suffer from poisoning if it licks its pads after walking over a surface that is wet with new paint which contains lead or turpentine or any colouring matter which may be harmful.

Immediately poisoning is suspected send for a Veterinary Surgeon, if possible advising him the name of the poison, so that he can bring the specific antidote or drug. Keep any vomited material for examination.

NOTES REGARDING POISONS CHART OPPOSITE

Emetics (to make a cat vomit) . . . The easiest to give is a piece of ordinary washing soda, hazel nut size, pushed down the throat like a pill . . . Otherwise give a teaspoonful of salt in 4 teaspoonfuls of water to drink (see page 93).

Laxative . . . Lik-a-Med Laxative—double dose—or Epsom Salts or Glauber Salts—enough to cover a sixpence.

In all cases of poisoning do not give any food for at least 24 hours.
In severe cases always call a Veterinary Surgeon since home treatment is inadequate. The details opposite are as a guide for home first-aid and milder cases.

148

POISONS CHART

See notes at foot of opposite page

POISON	EFFECTS	ANTIDOTE, etc.	FOOD, etc.
ARSENIC In weed killers, sheep dips, etc.	Nausea and vomit. Pupils dilated. Abdominal pains. Staggers. Dark colour diarrhoea. Fatal dose causes convulsions then paralysis and death	Give an EMETIC before convulsions start and later a LAXATIVE. Injections by Vet.	Oil or milk with beaten-up white of egg frequently. Keep patient warm and quiet in darkened room. Give a Sedative Tablet in milk
STRYCHNINE Rats, etc., poisons	Quickly fatal. Small doses can have a cumulative effect — nervousness, fright, jerky and stiffness of neck and back	Give an EMETIC before convulsions start. Then later a Sedative Tablet crushed in milk	Same as above
PHOSPHORUS Rat, etc., poisons	Shivery and weak. Vomit greenish with garlic smell and luminous in dark. Thirst, diarrhoea. Lips jaundiced yellow, may cough. Death 2–3 hours up to 2–3 days	Give a good dose of Epsom or Glauber Salts or Lik-a-Med. Sulphate of Copper (Bluestone) is the antidote—if available give Kittens 1 grain, Cats 2 grains	Do not give oils or fats or milk or anything greasy
LEAD From licking paint off paws, etc. Trace the source and remedy this	Saliva at mouth. Constipation—then diarrhoea and vomiting. Partial paralysis. Spasms of forelegs. If taken over a period —thin blue line around gums	Give a good dose of Epsom or Glauber Salts in milk or olive oil or milky food AT ONCE. Repeat after a few hours. Give raw egg beaten up in milk after the first dose	Olive oil, sardine oil, etc. Lactol and gruel
SULPHATE OF AMMONIA From dressing used on grass lawns	First stimulates, then depresses. Shivery. Pulse slow. Little if any vomit	Give an EMETIC, followed by plenty of water to keep the kidneys operating	Give glucose or sugar in milk and keep warm
ALKALIS Caustic Soda, Quicklime, etc.	See also burns	Give an acid drink, such as plenty of vinegar or lemon juice in water	Give olive oil, barley water, arrowroot, isinglass to soothe, etc.
ACIDS Nitric, Sulphuric, Spirits of Salts, etc.	See also burns	Give Milk of Magnesia, or failing this, bicarbonate of soda, in milk to drink	ditto
D.D.T. and WARFARIN	Vomiting and gastritis. Loss of appetite. Nervous tremors, fits and convulsions.	Give an EMETIC and after vomiting give a NON-OILY LAXATIVE. If D.D.T. is on the coat, remove all traces (Vitamin K is the antidote for Warfarin)	Give glucose or sugar in Lactol or milk to drink. Keep cat warm and quiet

149

POT BELLY

This condition, when it occurs in young kittens, is usually due to infestation by worms or by injudicious feeding.

The diet should be attended to and should consist principally of concentrated food, such as Lactol, with occasionally a little raw meat mixed with dry crushed Lactol Biscuits or Energol. Lintox Tonic should also be given to strengthen the digestive organs.

See Feeding Kittens, Roundworms, also Dropsy regarding " Pot Belly " in adult cats.

PYORRHOEA

Pyorrhoea is very often the result of excess tartar which has been allowed to form on the teeth, creating a septic condition of the gums and bad breath. In severe cases where it has secured a firm hold (with diseased gums and loosening of the teeth) then extraction of the teeth by a Veterinary Surgeon is necessary. In the earlier stages, however, development can be arrested by the use of a Tooth Scraper, and a mouth wash. See Teeth.

RABIES—Hydrophobia, Madness

Rabies is a notifiable disease and any cases must be notified to the Police.

No serious outbreaks have occurred in dogs or cats in Britain outside of quarantine establishments since 1918, due to the strict regulations for stamping out this very contagious virus disease. Australia, Norway, Sweden, Denmark and Holland are also clear of rabies and other countries are gradually introducing quarantine establishments. Cats are however far less liable to rabies than are dogs. The affected animal becomes wild and savage with a vacant wild stare—even biting itself on its legs and underneath.

After 2 or 3 days the animal becomes gradually paralysed, unable to close its mouth and there is profuse saliva. Death follows after a few days.

Any suspected animals must be isolated immediately and kept confined where they cannot harm other animals or humans. The bite of a rabid animal can be fatal to humans **and any human bitten by a rabid animal needs urgent medical attention**. If rabies is suspected a Veterinary Surgeon must be called in as quickly as possible.

RHEUMATISM

Cats are much less susceptible to rheumatism than dogs but the various forms of rheumatism, lumbago, etc., can occur in all animals just as in humans and are usually due to draughty or damp conditions, insufficient bedding, also lack of sunlight. Even puppies and kittens are sometimes attacked by rheumatism, giving rise to fever with high temperature, and one or more hot, swollen limbs, loss of appetite and constipation. Careful nursing is essential, with warmth.

In adult cats the animal walks with stiffened limbs and arched back . . . or the muscles tensed and often quivering, movement obviously difficult.

Treatment.—Sherley's Rheumatine Tablets will ease the pain and the stiffness; also give a dose of Lik-a-Med Laxative Cream once or twice a week as it is important to keep the bowels open. Warmth is essential.

Diet.—Fish or tripe mixed with rice or Lactol Meal or Biscuits and Energol, also milk puddings, etc. Red meat should be avoided for a time.

See also Arthritis and Paralysis.

RICKETS

Rickets in kittens is not so prevalent as formerly but when this complaint does occur, it is usually caused by kittens having been fed on a diet deficient in Vitamin D. The cat's own milk is three times richer than cow's milk and the pregnant queen needs extra-special nourishment beforehand and whilst suckling to provide adequate nourishment, in order to avoid weakness in her kittens. The kittens, too, need extra-special foods until they are fully grown.

Rickets is caused essentially by:—

(a) Lack of Vitamin D ⎫
(b) Absence of sunlight ⎬ These are vitally necessary.
(c) Unsatisfactory housing (perhaps in dark sheds with lack of exercise).
(d) Unsatisfactory feeding, where the diet fails to provide the right proportions of Calcium and Phosphorus salts.

As with children, the danger of rickets can be completely avoided and these are the essentials:—

(1) Correct feeding of the queen before mating and whilst she is carrying, also whilst she is feeding her kittens.

(2) Correctly supplementing the queen with Lactol whilst the kittens are suckling and after they are weaned.

(3) Feeding Lactol and Lactol Meal to the kittens during and after weaning.

(4) Good housing and exercising facilities and adequate sunlight.

Before mating give the queen at least a fortnight's course of Lintox Tonic, which contains essential phosphates and vitamins. During pregnancy feed her daily with Lactol which contains Vitamin D. After kittening plenty of Lactol is needed for sound bone building in the suckling kittens. Do not give liquid paraffin but give Lik-a-Med when a laxative is needed. Avoid any excess of yeast, oatmeal, maizemeal or foods containing these.

Kittens fed regularly on Lactol and Lactol Biscuits and Energol receive the necessary quota of Vitamin D which modern scientific investigation has proved to be absolutely essential to avoid rickets.

It is also advisable to worm kittens occasionally because, whilst worms will not cause rickets, they tend to sap the vitality of the animal and induce a state of pre-disposition towards the disease.

Symptoms.—The joints are enlarged, especially the knees, hocks and stifles. The forelegs become bowed because the bones become bent when bearing weight, and the ankles weak, so that the kitten walks on the backs of the legs instead of the feet. The back legs are crooked and the hocks turned inwards, this latter condition being termed cow-hock. The spine is often affected and curved, and the bones of the face may appear to be swollen. **In bad cases the kitten seems in constant pain and cries when it moves or is touched.**

Treatment.—Once the disease is established, the kitten should be given a daily dose of halibut liver oil capsules, kept in a more suitable place and fed on a diet consisting of Lactol, Lactol Meal and meat; the meat is best given on a large bone so that the kitten can gnaw it off as he likes. It is also desirable to give the kitten a teaspoonful of Energol well mixed in with his food, and Lintox Tonic according to directions.

Where sunlight is infrequent then a course of ultra-violet ray treatment is of value if started early—given only a few minutes each day whilst the kitten is asleep, or with eyes covered.

Splints and bandages, if used, must be under veterinary supervision. In a really serious case where the kitten is only half the size he ought to be, with elbows out, legs bowed, and with the hind legs in a similar distorted condition, and there is also indigestion and diarrhoea with a " pot-bellied " condition, the kindest course is to have him painlessly destroyed—in any event a great deal of time and money would be needed to effect any improvement.

RUPTURE.—See Hernia.

SCABIES.—See Mange.

SCALDS.—See also Burns.

Hot water or steam scalds are treated in the same way as burns, but it should be remembered that a scalded area may not be so readily located as a burn which singes the hair, and it may be some time before a scab appears. Where scalding is extensive, there is a great degree of shock, and veterinary treatment is essential to relieve pain.

<h2 style="text-align:center;">SICKNESS (TRAVEL)</h2>

Many cats are sick when riding in a motor vehicle, and some when in a train. Training from kittenhood to travel in a closed basket standing on the floor of the car prevents sickness. Never let a cat sit on the seat or watch out of the window. Once the travel sickness habit has been acquired the condition cannot be cured permanently, but a dose of Sherley's Travel Sickness Tablets given about an hour before starting will generally prevent sickness on that journey. The dose should vary according to the size of the cat, as directed on the packet.

See also Sending Cats by Rail, and Gastritis.

<h2 style="text-align:center;">SKIN DISEASES</h2>

See Eczema, Nettlerash, and Parasites.

<h2 style="text-align:center;">SPRAINS</h2>

Cats usually land safely from heights due to their amazing sense of balance and their light weight, but they can sprain a tendon or a ligament escaping from dogs chasing them, especially the stifle

153

joint (corresponding to the knee of a human being), which is situated in the hind leg between the hock and the hip and is a weak joint easily injured. The cat goes very lame and carries the leg for some time afterwards, and if care is not taken, he may become permanently lame. The joint is swollen, especially on the inside, where a distinct swelling can be felt. It is also painful, especially if the foot is drawn forward, and when standing still the cat keeps on his toes with the foot of the injured limb just behind the other. Often it is difficult to tell whether there is a fracture of the bone. If the sprain does not appear easier after about 48 hours obtain veterinary attention as X-ray photographs may be necessary to check whether a bone is fractured.

If it is definitely only a sprain then give him absolute rest for a week or longer, and apply cold water dressings frequently (do not use liniment). Lik-a-Med Laxative and a light diet are necessary as the cat will not be able to take exercise for some time. Other joints when sprained should be treated in a similar way.

See also Fractures.

STINGS (Bees and Wasps)

Cats usually " paw " at Bees, Wasps, etc., and then play with them on the ground and are therefore more likely to be stung on or between the pads, seldom in the mouth or throat as is the case with dogs, which snap at and swallow bees, etc. If possible locate and remove the bee sting. The cat may need a sedative before he will permit the sting to be found and removed. Wasps do not leave their sting.

For Bee Stings and Wasp Stings—the best first-aid is to dab on household Ammonia—diluted one part to 4 parts of water. If not available swab with bicarbonate of soda—one teaspoon per cup of water or apply raw onion or a blue bag or a dab of moistened washing soda.

TUBERCULOSIS

This was once quite a common disease in cats and is very contagious and dangerous to human beings, children in particular become victims if too fond of and cuddly over the domestic cat suffering from T.B.

Usually the source of the infection was the drinking of infected cow's milk. Fortunately in Britain and many other countries we very seldom encounter tuberculosis in cats from this cause, since infected cow's milk is no longer sold, the disease having been eliminated from our herds by 1961. One should not overlook the disease in cat meat from knackers' yards or in countries where slaughterhouses are not subject to meat inspection.

Cats, can, of course, also carry the human form of tuberculosis so it cannot be emphasised too strongly that any chronic cough accompanied by gradual wasting should always be thoroughly investigated by a Veterinary Surgeon in view of the risk to human beings, and obviously if this disease is detected the only possible thing is to have the cat painlessly put to sleep.

The symptoms are very slow in developing and loss of weight and general condition become apparent after a time. The coat tends to " stare " and there is sometimes although not always a cough. If one can take the temperature every 8 hours or so for a period it will be found to waver up and down between normal 101.5°F. and 102.5°F. (38.6°C. to 39.2°C.) or even 103°F. (39.4°C.). In advanced cases where the cat is obviously ill, the eyes can become affected, at first one eye then often both eyes. The glands in the abdomen become enlarged and can be felt when the abdominal wall is manipulated between the fingers by an expert.

The kidneys can be affected, in fact there is no internal organ that cannot be affected once tuberculosis has really got hold. There is no safe treatment which can be advocated and the only thing that can be done is to have the unfortunate animal put to sleep as soon as possible.

A medical check-up on all members of the family who are " contacts " is most important, so be sure to report the facts to your doctor.

TUMOURS

Tumours are hard swellings which develop gradually over a period of days or weeks and unlike abscesses, are not as a rule painful. There is no fever as is the case when an abscess is forming. Tumours may develop externally or internally and particularly on elderly cats, and may be on almost any part or any organ of the body. A tumour may be one of two types . . . **benign** . . . which eventually stops growing, whereas **malignant** tumours are cancerous and will continue to grow and reproduce in parts near or far from the site of the original.

Tumours are very frequently found in the milk glands of queens; they are quite small at first and may remain so for a long time, then, often without apparent cause, they commence to grow, sometimes becoming very large. See Breast.

In all cases of suspected tumour it is advisable to obtain early veterinary advice; it is useless to apply drugs—the only treatment is surgical, and the operation should be performed without delay if there is the least sign of growth in the tumour. The earlier the operation is performed the better the chance of recovery. If the growth is a malignant (cancerous) type, early recurrences and spreading throughout other parts of the body are to be expected and in such cases it is kinder to put the cat to sleep.

WOMB—DISEASE OF
Inflammation of Womb—**Metritis**
Pus in the Womb—**Pyometra**

There are various causes of this and its presence may be indicated by differing symptoms. Loss of appetite and dullness occur, the cat is thirsty, and there are usually from two to three degrees of fever. The cat may vomit.

It is often difficult to recognise the disease in its early stages, so often unnoticed until it has assumed the chronic state characterised by enlargement of the womb (the abdomen becoming large and pendulous) by loss of flesh across the loins, and by the blood-stained discharge from the vagina, which may have been present but unobserved in the earlier phase, becoming more profuse and having an unpleasant odour. The symptoms gradually increase in severity, the cat becoming weak and ill and sometimes refusing all food.

Metritis most often occurs after kittening, usually after a difficult labour or because of ill health on the part of the mother or due to complications or miscarriage or from clumsy handling in attempts to assist the arrival of one or more kittens, any of which causes can lead to germ infection. Metritis is a serious condition and can cause blood poisoning and possible death of the queen or at least difficulty in rearing the kittens.

Where any disease of the womb is suspected it is best to seek veterinary attention as soon as possible. The early injection of modern antibiotics by a Veterinary Surgeon will help to avoid serious consequences and therefore the owner is strongly urged to obtain veterinary help as soon as possible. Unless experienced, it is not wise to attempt to syringe out the uterus or use a catheter or other methods since this may cause complications of a serious nature, whereas so much good can be done by one or two injections of antibiotics.

In Pyometra, which is suppuration (formation of pus) in the womb of the cat, there is occasionally the added symptom of vomiting. Pyometra can best be remedied by surgical operation.

WORMS.—See Parasites.

WOUNDS

First, trim away the hair. If the wound is a straight tear or cut it should first be thoroughly washed with diluted Amplexol or Kennel Fluid, then sewn up with thick surgical silk, covered over with dry boracic wool or gauze, and bandaged. Remove the stitches after a week then treat with Sherley's Veterinary Ointment.

If it is a jagged wound it is a more difficult problem and needs veterinary attention, but if none is available, after being well cleansed, it should be treated as above. If a bandage cannot be applied, bathe this type of wound three or four times a day with diluted Sherley's Antiseptic Lotion or Amplexol.

In severe wounds the cat should be prevented from licking the wound by being made to wear a wide leather collar (see page 131).

WOUNDS (Punctured)

These are wounds which, although appearing small on the skin, are so deep that they penetrate the structures underneath. They are the most dangerous type because the skin often heals before the under structures, poisonous germs being imprisoned, and an abscess forms. There is no danger of this occurring if the wound is kept open until the discharge has quite ceased. Trim away the hair, apply hot boracic lotion fomentations and plug a piece of ribbon-gauze or lint smeared with Sherley's Veterinary Ointment into the wound. This gauze or lint should be changed night and morning, and otherwise treat the wound in the ordinary way. Burn all soiled dressings and rinse the hands in Sherley's Antiseptic Lotion, then wash.

A bad punctured wound is often caused by the bite of a dog, a canine tooth or tusk causing the damage.

The advent of **Antibiotics** has completely revolutionised and simplified the treatment of wounds. With all severe wounds we do particularly recommend that the cleansing, stitching and treatment is entrusted to a veterinary surgeon. Severely wounded animals which a few years ago would have had to be put to sleep are now healed quickly with antibiotics.

157

CONCERNING LACTOL

The Ideal Food for Kittens, Puppies and other Young Animals

Scientific research in the rearing of small animals has proved that the use of cow's milk, goat's milk and ordinary powdered milk foods, although apparently cheaper, are extremely unsatisfactory owing to the essential difference in the composition.

Bitch's milk and queen's milk contain far more fat and casein, ten times as much albumin, and less sugar and water compared with cow's milk.

When fed on cheaper or unsuitable mixtures, kittens and puppies have to take far too much water with troublesome results—indigestion, diarrhoea, distended stomach, etc.—often fatal.

Lactol approaches more to the milk of any healthy bitch or queen than any other food or preparation and is the perfect food for litters and for pregnant and nursing mothers, because it contains the essential proteins, fats, casein and albumin—**in easily digested form.**

Lactol enables expectant mothers to assimilate the lime salts in food, thus ensuring the foundation of good bone, flesh and teeth.

Lactol is manufactured under the strictest hygienic conditions and is free from pathogenic or harmful bacteria. Kittens and puppies are successfully reared from birth on Lactol—it is the perfect supplement when litters are large—perfect for weaning, and also for feeding rabbits, silver foxes, chinchillas and even newly-born foals and lambs.

Hand-reared from birth on SHERLEY'S LACTOL

Bred and hand-reared by MRS. GRACE POND, F.Z.S.

....
....
....
....
....
....
....
....
....
....
....
....
....
....
....
....
....
....
....
....
....
....
....
....

Nearest Vet. _____Phone No.
_____

Nearest Sherley Stockist_____Phone No.
_____